This wonderful collection of short patie
narrative of life and love and loss. How
narrative' but a reminder that we are all t
all meet the same fate in the end. It follows, therefore, that death and dying
should naturally form part of public discourse, of family conversation.
So-called 'advance care planning', a concept often misnamed 'advanced'
care planning, is not in fact advanced or complex after all. This book
illustrates it in its simplicity. We only really need to say what we want,
what we don't want and who will speak for us. Importantly, the healthcare
professionals we meet along the way should be adequately equipped to sit
comfortably with us in conversation about death and dying. This book is a
roadmap for us all.

Aoife Lowney, Consultant in Palliative Medicine, John Radcliffe Hospital
and Sobell House Palliative Care Service, Oxford, UK

This book and the short stories it contains should be of interest to those
who will die (spoiler alert: that's all of us) and for those of us who look
after the dying. These stories are a window into people's lives at their
most vulnerable: when they are dying. Some of these people know what is
happening, but many do not – until it is too late to talk about it. Like almost
all of us, they take with them on this final journey the people who love
them, who travel along as far as they can, to the point of departure. Sadly,
time for meaningful conversations is one thing that has been built out of
the modern medical world. This book is about when such communication
has not happened – or when occasionally it has. So read these stories and
understand that we can do this better.

Sally Greenaway, Palliative Care Physician, Westmead Hospital, NSW,
Sydney, Australia

The topic of death and dying is not something that we talk about in our
culture. In the pages that follow individuals are honoured as their stories
unfold. We learn about building compassion in our community, and
relationships with those close to us. Death is commonplace, and how we
plan and spend our time preparing for it will guide the final episode of our
life. This book helps us to transform our relationship to ageing, mortality,
dying and death – whether expected or unexpected – so that we may
rekindle the way we live and help to break down the mystery. Through
reading the stories you will understand ways in which you can improve
quality of life and better prepare for death. Take time to grieve and talk with
counsellors and support organisations that can help.

Joan Carlini, Chair, Gold Coast Hospital and Health Service Consumer
Advisory Group, Queensland, Australia

All royalties from the sale of this book support research to improve end of life for older people.

When the Time Comes

Stories from the end of life

Magnolia Cardona MB BS, PhD
and
Ebony Lewis BN, MIPH

With a Foreword by
Dr John Kellet

and an Afterword by
Dr Norman Swan

Hammersmith Books Limited
London, UK

First published in 2021 by Hammersmith Health Books
– an imprint of Hammersmith Books Limited
4/4A Bloomsbury Square, London WC1A 2RP, UK
www.hammersmithbooks.co.uk

The information contained in this book is for educational purposes only. It is the result of the study and the experience of the authors. Whilst the information and advice offered are believed to be true and accurate at the time of going to press, neither the authors nor the publisher can accept any legal responsibility or liability for any errors or omissions that may have been made or for any adverse effects which may occur as a result of following the recommendations given herein. Always consult a qualified medical practitioner if you have any concerns regarding your health.

British Library Cataloguing in Publication Data: A CIP record of this book is available from the British Library.

Print ISBN 978-1-78161-190-6
Ebook ISBN 978-1-78161-191-3

Commissioning editor: Georgina Bentliff
Typeset by: Evolution Design & Digital Ltd
Cover design by: Madeline Meckiffe
Cover image by: Madeline Meckiffe based on a concept by Indigenous
    artist Anne Dillon
Production: Helen Whitehorn, Path Projects Ltd
Printed and bound by: TJ Books Ltd, Cornwall, UK

Table of contents

About the authors

Dr Magnolia Cardona is a former GP, public health practitioner and current associate professor of health services research. She is a passionate advocate for the rights of older people dying of natural causes to not be over-treated with low-value care and instead have a dignifying end of life through aligning treatments with patients' values and planning in advance. She arranged her own first advance care directive before the birth of her child by elective caesarean, as she envisaged the possibility of things going wrong and had the urgency for planning what clinicians and her family should do if she couldn't decide. She now conducts research with patients, families and clinicians on ways to improve the end-of-life experience for all.

Nurse Ebony Lewis is experienced in emergency medicine and geriatrics, a skills combination that has made her highly aware of the needs of older people to be treated compassionately at a place of their choice, including their own home rather than in the emergency department environment or the intensive care unit. She loves talking to older patients, visiting them at home for their health assessments and helping them express their values and preferences before they become critically ill. She was awarded an international prize for her research into advance care documentation and is now undertaking her PhD studies on frailty.

The contributors

Chapters have been contributed by:

Margaret Nicholson	Ebony Lewis	Hatem Alkhouri
Amy Dunlop	Kelly Land	Vitor Rocha
Claire Alexander	Lucie Rychetnik	Lucy Tinoco
Anne Dillon	Alejandro Delgado	Imelda Gilmore
Sabrina Palham	Velma Oswald	Harpreet Kalsi
Laura Hanly	Magnolia Cardona	

The contributors are sons, daughters, spouses, grandchildren, informal caregivers, trainees and health professionals caring for the people in these stories. They have given us their time and poured their hearts into these pages, either directly or indirectly through the editors. We hope you appreciate the wholehearted effort they put into making readers aware of what to consider doing or not doing *when the time comes* for you or your loved ones.

Acknowledgments

Our gratitude goes to all the contributing patients, families and clinicians for their willingness to give their time to share their very personal stories and for teaching us so many life lessons. This book would not have been possible without their perspectives. Our appreciation also goes to the Indigenous artist Anne Dillon whose painting inspired the book cover representing what this grieving journey is about: darkness followed by the colours of hope.

Special thanks go to our families for their patience, encouragement and understanding of our mission to change practice by normalising end-of-life conversations.

Foreword

Magnolia asked me to write this foreword a few days before I was about to have surgery. As a retired physician my perspective is rapidly changing from that of a provider to that of a consumer of healthcare. During the last few years, I have witnessed the deaths of some close relatives; this has caused me to reflect on the good and the bad aspects of modern healthcare. Over my 50-year career in medicine, the biggest change has been in the number of health professionals a patient is likely to encounter during an illness and the number of things that can be done to them. When I was a child, the family doctor was always available, affable and trusted. Few doubted his opinion, and if he decided you needed to see a specialist or to go to hospital, it was accepted that the situation was serious and the outcome uncertain. The 'truth' was only implied by knowing glances and muffled murmurs behind closed doors, and everyone agreed that nothing more could be done, and prayed for a 'happy release'. Nowadays everything has changed – there is always more that can be done, everyone knows someone who has tried this or that, and there is simply no limit to the number of opinions, investigations and possible treatments that might be considered. What has not changed during my career is the ability of physicians and patients wisely to control what, of all the ever-increasing options, should be done.

All of us know we are going to die, but most of us do not like to think about it too much. We may have imagined how we would prefer to die but might have considered there was little point in such morbid musing. Nowadays, however, everyone should think about what they want, and how they might control what happens *when the time comes*. No one should underestimate the ability of modern medicine to prolong life and suffering at enormous expense.

Fifty years ago, obtaining medical care was like asking someone for a lift in their car. You had some idea of the speed the car could travel, its level of safety and comfort, and getting the car to stop or go somewhere else was easy. Medical care today is more like flying on a commercial airliner. It is statistically far safer than a car ride, often not that comfortable, but once the flight has started, changing the destination is difficult and getting off is impossible. Even as a doctor I found it difficult to curb my colleagues' well-intentioned enthusiasm to do everything possible for my relatives, even though I knew most of their interventions were futile. Firstly, I had to be careful not to offend them or be thought of as a 'difficult relative' or a 'know-it-all' doctor, and I did appreciate how kind they all were and how hard they were trying to help. Secondly, I did not want them to think that I wanted active euthanasia, and thirdly, I also did not want to upset the rest of my family. The fact is that modern medical care, and intensive care in particular, is a complex system with many players set up to do everything to keep the patient alive as long as possible: once the system is set in motion it is very difficult for a single individual to stop it.

We are all different and have different desires. What I wanted as a young man was not what I want now. At the end of our lives we might all be surprised at what we really value. I have seen distraught children fly their dying mother to a far-flung clinic for another round of chemotherapy when all she wanted was to visit for the last time the small primary school she attended as a child.

Who knows why she wanted this, but she did. Her children did not understand, so she travelled with them to die abroad and never saw her old school again.

Each chapter of this book describes how different people have encountered death and dying. It is an important book to read: it provides no answers but may make you wiser.

Dr John Kellet
Nenagh, Ireland, September 2020

Introduction

Magnolia Cardona

Technological advances have increasingly benefited patients but have also led us to hold higher expectations of immortality through medical 'miracles'. However, sometimes demanding these health services when it is too late for them to be of benefit perpetuates the delivery of non-beneficial treatments and low-value care that is potentially harmful to individuals and the health system.

The concept of a 'good death' seems a contradiction in terms. However, we gain a clearer picture when we think of preventing or controlling pain; managing anxiety, breathlessness and frailty; avoiding unnecessary surgical procedures; discontinuing uncomfortable treatments; ceasing futile and potentially detrimental medications; and generally being in control of the quality of a life at the 'tail-end'. It can be more satisfying if we can do it on our and our loved one's own terms.

This book is a collection of true stories written by relatives of older people dying from chronic incurable illness and by experienced nurses who have been involved in the process. We have gathered these experiences to share them with the public and help raise awareness of the need to discuss end-of-life wishes in advance. While we acknowledge that the topic of death is taboo in some cultures, and that the grieving process can differ across countries and from individual to individual, we have learned from the suffering of many the importance of being open about our personal choices of how we die, be it the place of death or the initiation or withdrawal of aggressive treatment when death approaches. We have learned that it is important to improve the experience of death from chronic incurable illness, or from plain old age.

Sometimes the authors of these stories have been involved in making decisions on behalf of loved ones at the time they were dying. In the process they have gone through the dilemma of not being certain of prior patient preferences, having unrealistic expectations of what technology can achieve, but ultimately needing to feel reassured that they are 'doing the right thing' with or without all the relevant information. The satisfaction of honouring patients' wishes can help make difficult end-of-life decisions more bearable for healthcare providers, minimise regret among surviving families, and enable a healthier grieving process.

In this compilation of short stories we have honoured the details of each individual account but have changed the names to protect confidentiality. We hope the messages in each, some harrowing and some uplifting, will encourage you to think about your preferences for place of death and the level of intervention you would tolerate or be willing to forego. Perhaps these true stories from the end of life will motivate you to have a conversation with a loved one, or express your wishes (or theirs) in writing, with the help of a healthcare professional to prevent those unnecessarily heroic treatments that will not make a difference to your survival and could potentially impair the quality of your end of life. You don't need to have a terminal illness to discuss your end-of-life care preferences. The stories here remind us that, despite our best efforts, we are not immortal yet, and that while we are still able we can be proactive in preparing for the final transition, to improve the experience for both the dying and the living left behind.

1

Grandma: preparing for death but living life to the full

Death is largely considered a taboo subject, reserved for solemn occasions, inviting fear, uncertainty and despair. But not for Grandma. Grandma has her own funeral planned and paid for (although she's not sure that she's got the perfect photo of herself for the occasion, so when her grand-children visit she continually asks them to take funeral-appropriate headshots as she poses, smiling sombrely). She has all her wishes written down, her bucket list (almost) ticked off, and a clear idea of what she would and would not want in the case that she were incapacitated and no longer able to communicate her wishes.

Grandma has had this all organised since her early 70s. But don't get me wrong, she is not a morbid person. She is not all doom and gloom to be around. In fact, at age 83, she goes to two yoga classes a week, a dance class, a stretch class, and plays bridge with friends two or three days a week. She goes on outings to the theatre with a local seniors group, is a member of a local walking group (and she walks fast!), plus every second weekend she seems to be going to some kind of birthday party, ranging from 'young' friends' 70ths, to her older friends 90th and 100th birthdays. She's active on email and Skype as she doesn't want to miss any crucial life developments within her family or social circle.

She makes the most of her life, and she wants to live. But she also wants to be prepared, and we all know that death is inevitable. Grandma knows that when her time comes she does not want to be kept alive with machines, with no realistic hope of regaining the quality of life she currently enjoys. So she has set her wishes down on paper. She has let her doctor know what her wishes are, and thanks to a forward-thinking initiative set up by her local health district, she has an emergency folder kept in her fridge to be found by the paramedics if ever she were to have a medical emergency, telling them the ins and outs of her wishes, and the contact names and numbers of her next of kin.

As part of her preparations one night she invited her son and daughter to a 'death dinner' at her house. The first thing they noticed on arrival was a yellow Planning Ahead[1] sticker on her front door. It was odd but they didn't think anything of it. Her collectors' teacups, plates and saucers were perfectly laid out on the table, with salads, meats, fruit, and freshly made cheesecake for dessert, as if she wanted hot dinner and afternoon tea combined all in one. It all felt like a regular Sunday visit, her hostess generosity on display, the homely cooking smell as they remembered it when they lived with her, and her routine unchanged. Except this time, right next to the cutlery, on each of the placemats, there was a large yellow envelope – same shade of yellow as the door sticker – not to be opened until instructed. It contained a copy of the document Grandma wanted to share: her advance care directive. But the children did not know. Her plan was to go through it soon after the main meal and then serve dessert.

Once they had finished their meal and after a few minutes of small talk about the weather and local gossip, Grandma started her speech about how much she valued autonomy, how she was satisfied with her life so far and her longstanding friendships and how well her children had turned out. Then she came to the point:

'I've been to my family doctor to discuss an important topic I am putting the finishing touches on.'

Her children gave each other an alarmed look. Their hearts sank. They assumed she was going to tell them she had an incurable illness or had suicidal ideation, or worse, that she had a new boyfriend and was going to change her will to leave the cottage and lovely memorabilia to him.

The truth was far from that. Grandma was in a very good mood, still thankfully single, and in rude good health for her age. She told them about the Planning Ahead resources and the Dying Matters movement: 'I read about the campaign in the local newspaper and I have no time to waste,' she said decisively. 'Apparently there is a website you can also look up!'

She informed her children of her wishes for supportive care and emphasised 'no tubes or machines to keep me alive'; she also told them where to find the necessary documents if needed. Where else but in the fridge? Yes, that's what the campaign recommends. She had used her local health district papers as a template for the evening, ticking off each part as it was completed.

- 'Funeral arrangements' – Tick
- 'Next of kin informed' – Tick
- 'Bucket list items' – Tick
- 'Make sure you leave nothing important unsaid to your loved ones'...

Briefly looking up from the list at her bewildered son and daughter, Grandma said 'Well ...of course I love you' – Tick!

Grandma was efficiently getting things done. Not one to wear her heart on her sleeve, this was a rare and important expression of love for her son and daughter.

Although it came as a surprise to them – parents themselves – that Grandma knew so much about the importance of planning ahead, the children felt amazed and relieved she was not mortally ill and was so much in control of her affairs. Besides, she gave them no choice! Far from being a morbid activity, Grandma's willingness to put her wishes down on paper had in fact relieved the burden of difficult decision-making from her family. Just the way she wanted it to be. That was Grandma's approach, and they knew there was no point in debating.

But Grandma didn't stop at that. Last holiday she invited me, her grandchild, to drive around with her to visit friends in her age group. I was shocked to discover it was to give them the gift of quality end-of-life by bringing along a blank sample of an advance care directive for them to complete too. And I got to hear about the purpose of the yellow envelope in the fridge and the meaning of the yellow sticker at the front door.

Grandma lives a full and active life, and her family and loved ones all hope that she continues to do so for many years. But life is unpredictable, and it is a comfort to know that she has set down her wishes with such clarity, so if things ever do take a turn for the worse, her family can know fully how to honour her wishes.

What do you think?

- How would you broach the subject of end-of-life wishes with your family without being confronting?
- Would you be bold enough to hold a 'death dinner' or a 'death café' where a group of people meet to drink tea/coffee to discuss death and dying to help them normalise that topic (see https://deathcafe.com/what/)?
- Like Grandma in this story, how willing are you to discuss your funeral plans with your family today, and why? If you avoid the subject altogether, why is that?
- How has this story changed your mind about discussing these matters?

2

What time is the right time?

They were just little things at first, barely noticeable, hardly worth mentioning. But they were a warning and had we read the signs better, we might have done things differently, or sooner. Or would we?

When Nick misplaced his wallet once, twice, three times, we all looked until we found it. He was relieved and ever so grateful each time. When he left his card in the ATM, we thought it could happen to anyone. When the garage door was left wide open an entire day, we were just glad no one had got in. How lucky were we only the glass stove top shattered and just the underside of the kitchen cupboards burnt, when he left the gas on all day. Certainly this was more serious than misplacing a wallet, but the explanation was quite plausible.

His brother was visiting from a faraway city and they had planned a day out. He had prepared a casserole for dinner for all of us but hadn't noticed that the gas was still on as they left. Could have happened to anyone.

It was a lovely warm October day for our grandson's christening and we organised a BBQ lunch after church. Nick took charge as he was the BBQ king. He was a great chef and a good host but at some point the cooking stopped and he never went back to it. My brother took over. Nick didn't seem to notice.

These episodes, and others, didn't happen in quick succession. They were spread across the years so that they appeared separate and stand-alone at the time. Only when I look back can I see an accumulating series of events. It would be 13 years after Nathan's christening before Nick would need care, so you'd think there was ample opportunity to broach 'the subject'. But we never did and really it didn't seem necessary. After all, we had updated our Wills and organised Powers of Attorney. The house we had built was in my name only. Nick insisted on this because my Dad had given me the land. My Will therefore stipulated that if I died first, the house would transfer to Nick for life, ensuring he would always have a roof over his head. So what we did seemed enough. The documents made our wishes known, our drivers licences carried notification that we were organ donors and as an Advance Care Directive was never mentioned we were satisfied we'd covered all bases.

Formalising our wishes in relation to how we wanted to die didn't happen, but that's not to say that we didn't talk about dying. We did. The topic came up at different times prompted by something we'd read or saw on the news or heard on the radio. We didn't actually initiate it but whatever got it started, I was in no doubt about what Nick wanted, or more precisely, what he didn't want.

You see, Nick was 26 years older than me. Ask anyone who knew us and they'll all say the same. I was the love of his life, so it was important to him that he stay healthy and well. And he was. He had energy, strength, experience and technical know-how. He could build a wall or wire a lamp, ride a motorcycle or drive a tow truck. He was happy tinkering and being busy. He read the paper every day and finished a book a month. We had long before resolved any concerns about our age difference but nevertheless he was aware that the day would come when he would no longer be able to keep doing the things he loved and, worse, be unable to care for himself and me. What he didn't want was to be a burden on me. But for others to care for him was also not an option. So he was quite vocal whenever the topic came up: no way was I to be his nursemaid and no one else was going to wipe his bum, shower, dress or feed him. 'Just shoot me,' he'd say, 'I'll drive myself over a cliff.'

But lots of people have said similar things. It was never followed up with 'So what do you really want?' It was easier to utter the throwaway lines than actually have a serious conversation. Why? Because it was just that. Serious. Who wanted to talk mortality when they were feeling so alive? What time is the right time to talk about such things?

'Just shoot me' was emphatic but hardly a healthcare directive. It was about ending his life quickly rather than lingeringly caring for him. The topic of euthanasia was in the public domain but I don't remember similar discussions about comfort care. If we had taken time to talk seriously, more than likely we would have talked about nursing home versus staying at home. And Nick was quite adamant: 'No nursing home for me!'

To be honest, I don't think I really believed Nick would need care. He'd had his coronary artery by-pass when he was 64 and, in his own words, had a new lease of life. If he was going to shuffle off this mortal coil, I imagined it would have something to do with his heart, but not for years yet, and that it would be quick. His father was 92 when he died and his brother 96. I anticipated that he too would live long but never expected it would be via the slow road to Alzheimer's.

In 2012, after six months' trial on medication, the geriatrician decided that there had been no improvement and the medication was ceased. An aged care assessment followed and Nick was deemed to require high-level care. The report reflected the family's wish that Nick remain at home for as long as possible. I was still working part-time and my job meant that I was only away for 2-3 hours at a time a few days a week. We managed quite well for about 12 months by organising his shower, shave and clothes and preparing meals in advance. He was still happy pottering in the yard and wanted to stay active around the house, but eventually became more and more tired and tended to sleep a lot. Unfortunately this meant he was awake all through the night and in the end, neither of us slept. Because he wasn't unwell, didn't use lots of medication, wasn't bed-ridden, was still mobile albeit a little slower, we persevered. Until the day he left the house. It was only through sheer luck he was discovered by a neighbour and brought safely home. So locks were changed, keys hidden and from then on life was more nerve-racking. He was testy, worried that people were trying to break into his room, the brats (our grandchildren) were stealing his medals or his wallet. He didn't see the need for a shower and couldn't find the loo when he needed it.

He tied his shoelaces in a variety of sailors' knots which were impossible to untie. He tripped up the stairs and fell down them. We worried for his safety. Conversation about anything meaningful was impossible. We worried for him and we worried for us.

The time had come to consider care but any opportunity to discuss his wishes had been missed. Even though I knew his feelings about death and dying, they weren't committed to paper. The decision to place him in care was the hardest and saddest I'd ever faced. The adjustment was difficult for everyone but eventually the nursing home became 'home' for Nick.

The discussion with the nursing home regarding advance care planning didn't happen until well into his residency there. Eventually we had the discussion and completed the necessary forms. In the intervening period, Nick suffered breathing difficulties and was taken to Emergency where he was treated for pneumonia. His condition was very serious; however, he responded well to antibiotics and made a full recovery. At his next hospital admission about six months later, his condition was grave. He wasn't conscious and didn't regain consciousness. By then the paperwork reflected that there should be no intervention and he was given the appropriate comfort care.

In spite of this I couldn't help but feel that had he been able to enunciate his own wishes, they might have been different from those he had expressed all those years earlier. Might he have changed his mind? I doubt it really but I just wish he had recorded it. We had been together for almost 40 years and that first conversation had easily been 25 years earlier. I knew instinctively we had acted in the way Nick wanted, but it didn't stop that nagging uncertainty from creeping in.

The doctors accurately predicted that he would die in the next day or so and there was time to gather the family together. He was made very comfortable and, for the first time in a long time, he seemed at peace. The disease that agitated him and robbed him of his dignity was no longer evident. He got to 91 and by his own assessment was the luckiest man in the world.

What do you think?

- What do you make of the statement 'Who wanted to talk mortality when they were feeling so alive for a man in his 80s?'?
- When do you think is the right time to start the conversation about what you value most and what you would like to avoid in your last days?

3

An unexpected friendship

I met Susan for the first time on her birthday while she was in hospital. Susan was in her fifties and had been admitted to the Palliative Care Unit one week prior. She had suffered a pulmonary embolism (a blood clot in her lung), an acute complication of her disseminated cancer. Susan had been confined to her bed since admission, the breathlessness and exhaustion caused by the clot rendering it impossible to undertake basic day-to-day tasks or even speak in full sentences. She was receiving daily injections to assist in dissolving the clot; however, it was unclear how successful this would be.

I was a newly graduated Registered Nurse at the time, and this shift was like any other. During our morning 'hello round' we – the treating team on shift – introduced ourselves to Susan, as we did with every patient, and she told us it was her birthday. She wanted more than anything to get out of bed and celebrate with her family. We all knew it would likely be her last birthday. I was assigned to looking after Susan and we agreed to restructure the workload so I could spend more time with her, taking on as much of the physical burden of showering and dressing her as I could in order to reserve her energy for more important things – that is, her party.

We helped Susan into new clothes, her sisters came and did her hair and make-up and we all felt so pleased that we had enabled Susan to achieve what she wanted. With device alarms ringing, patients waiting and a myriad of nursing tasks to be completed,

I moved on with my day, the laughter and music of Susan's birthday celebration in the distant background.

It wasn't until after the end of my shift that I realised how meaningful my role had been. Susan's sister ran up to me as I walked to my car, she grabbed my arm and with tears in her eyes said 'thank you'. It was the most sincere thank you I have ever received. I suddenly felt overwhelmed by the significance of my role. How privileged I was, this inexperienced 23-year-old, to be able to make such a difference in people's lives.

Susan was exhausted for a few days afterwards, but since she had had a wonderful time that day, it was worth it.

I ended up being allocated as her nurse for a good portion of her stay on the unit. Whilst helping with her daily shower we chatted about our lives and I felt a special connection with her. This unplanned work schedule had led to an unexpected friendship. I knew how to make her feel comfortable by not always talking about her illness. And when we did mention the terminal illness (we both knew it) I didn't say 'It's going to be OK' or 'You'll pull through this', but I let her know I was there for her if she needed anything while in hospital. She understood I was prepared to do little things beyond nursing care, such as bring her sweet treats or magazines, talk about a TV show I had watched the night before, or help her make phone calls to her family when they couldn't visit.

In the sporadic chances I had to socialise with her during my shifts we laughed comparing notes about our different upbringings. I told her about my story of becoming a nurse because I had always felt rewarded helping others. She told me how grateful she was growing up in an extended family. She had an inflated sense of belonging I did not experience in the same way myself. I also groomed her hair and gave her a bit of make up as I believe in giving a sense of normality helps the soul, and even agree that pyjamas should be discontinued altogether to help patients recover;[2] Susan giggled at that and we didn't go that far.

Chapter 3

I also got to know her wonderful family – her sons, her sisters and her friends. It was a relief to know I was not her only lifeline and Susan wondered 'What would their lives be like after I'm gone?' I encouraged her to think that she was leaving a good legacy of love and determination and her memory would live on. They also were good at following Susan's mood cues and talked about all sorts of routine things and made jokes to distract her from the big menacing thing overshadowing their family. Some other times they touched hands without saying anything. There was no awkwardness despite the silences, just no need to say anything, as all of them knew the end could be near. I was constantly amazed at their resilience and positivity in caring not only for Susan but also for each other; a great testament to Susan's beautiful nature.

Susan gradually regained her independence; the treatment for the pulmonary embolism was successful that time, and she was discharged home a couple of weeks following her birthday. In fact, Susan had one more birthday after that. When the time came, she chose to die in the palliative care unit where we knew her and she knew us. We were 'her other family'. She died in that caring environment surrounded by her relatives, friends, and us on her third admission, one and a half years later.

What do you think?

- How confident or uncomfortable would you feel speaking with someone you knew who was in their last months or weeks of life? What would you talk about with them?
- How would you mentally equip yourself to support a friend or loved one in the end-of-life transition? Or, if you would avoid the situation, why is that?

4

Where is the manual for the family of the dying person?

I am an end-of-life doula – that is, a person without healthcare qualifications who offers non-medical support and information about the dying journey to patients and their families. I am exceedingly passionate about supporting those around me to have the best possible end of their days. I truly believe that being there with people at the end of their life is extremely important, especially to support their mind and spirit – the two aspects of holistic health that are often overlooked.

I wasn't always driven to work as an advocate on these matters. This changed radically in November 2016 when my mum, a kind, generous and wise 62-year-old soul, died from idiopathic pulmonary disease. These words translated into plain English mean 'a very rare kind of illness of the lungs for which there is no known cause or cure.'

'Why?' and 'How?' are the two key questions often asked when faced with an unexpected and unwanted diagnosis. Sometimes there is no rational or easy answer to 'Why?' or 'How?'. Mum very rarely drank, she didn't smoke, she had a balanced, healthy diet and exercised. So, when there is no clear-cut reason for why a deadly condition sets in, the mind searches for meaning and answers. That constant searching for a solution while our bodies slowly or quickly deteriorate can cause a great deal of emotional suffering. The next few months were hard and my focus was on supporting my family, especially my dad.

In the final week of Mum's life, my dad, brother and I kept vigil by her side, with the support of my sister-in-law, husband and extended family. We took turns sitting with her and holding her hand day and night for five days. She was scared and didn't want to be alone. One night, in the early hours of the morning, when it was my turn to sit with Mum, I heard a man in the room next door start to sob. His wife had died and there was no one with him to support him; he was all alone. At that moment I felt deeply drawn to work in end-of-life and palliative care.

So in early 2017, I started my training as an end-of-life doula for the primary purpose of feeling educated, prepared and confident to support those around me when it was their time. Since then, I have had the privilege of supporting colleagues, friends and family in their end-of-life journey. We leave this world as we enter it, dependent on others, yet there is a very big difference between birthing support and the support given when a person leaves this world.

One of the most valuable exercises I undertook as part of my training was to map my mum's journey – her disease trajectory from pre-diagnosis, through diagnosis and palliative care to dying, death and our bereavement. The purpose was to reflect and learn – what worked well, where was there good support? Where could questions have been asked? Where would support and information have been helpful?

In the pre-diagnosis stage, Mum was full of life and light, active in her community, did Zumba and attended Spanish class. Around 2013, she started having a persistent cough which wouldn't go away, bad reflux, lost weight and appetite, and the X-rays showed shadows in her lungs. The doctors couldn't figure it out and suggested lung biopsy, but Mum declined. She never liked medications or interventions.

The diagnosis stage commenced when in early 2016 Mum finally agreed to a lung biopsy. She was diagnosed with idiopathic pulmonary disease. By April her specialist told her she had a year to live at best. Mum's reaction to the look on Dad's and my faces when the specialist told us this was to laugh and say, 'I'm not about to die right now am I?' She tried medication available in other countries to prevent and slow disease progression but she couldn't tolerate the side effects. She was too fragile for a lung transplant – wouldn't survive. She became steadily weaker and frailer. I got married in August that year and Mum was very excited about the wedding. It gave her something to focus on. She was admitted to hospital the next month for further investigation.

I remember very clearly thinking during Mum's final months, 'Where's the book? Where's the manual? How can I make sure I am doing everything I can to help her to have a peaceful death? Is there a tick box? A cheat sheet?' I tried my best: I took her into the sunshine on cool winter days, massaged her hands and feet, encouraged her and Dad to start meditating daily. I practised aromatherapy and tried to coordinate her support rituals. I guided Mum in creating her own affirmation so she could have a strong mind and something to hold onto when the pain or suffering became too much. Something to bring her comfort was a little reading on a wall poster: 'I am strong, I am able, I am calm'. This was incredibly important to Mum. It was very hard for her, as it is for anyone who is still young and not ready to let go, to be unable to do the very things that make them who they are.

There was no manual or book for us caregivers, to travel this journey. We had to write it ourselves.

We then moved to the palliative phase. In September, after Mum had been in hospital for 1½ weeks no one could tell us what was happening. My cousin, who is a GP, came to visit. I told her we were feeling anxious and frustrated. She told us we had the right to call a family meeting with the treating doctor. She advocated for us and organised the meeting. The doctor told us to come outside and said, 'I'm not good with these sorts of things' – that is, telling us she was dying. I felt for him – our entire medical system is geared towards prolonging life, so when specialists are faced with how to talk about and deal with the end, it's hard. At that point in time though, I was upset. We just wanted to know what was going on and how best to support Mum. I asked about when we'd start palliative care and he said he'd already started by prescribing anti-anxiety medication. He also referred Mum to a local hospital palliative care service for in-home care. A very good friend of mine who was studying nursing at the time told me we should get Mum to complete her advance care directive (ACD). It was the first time I had heard about ACDs and it was difficult to hear and accept what we needed to prepare for.

The next two months were a steep learning curve – learning how to take care of Mum at home. Because she was under 65, she was not eligible for seniors' government subsidy, so we had to organise and hire a hospital bed, shower stool, wheelchair and commode, learn how to hold Mum, clean her and then try to provide her with social and spiritual support. Monks visited from the Buddhist temple a few times. We played Sikh hymns that gave her comfort. Guided meditation helped both Mum and Dad as did her affirmation, along with touch and being present. We created a family keepsake artwork that Mum contributed handprints to for her grand-daughter who was born six weeks after she died.

From this period, there were two key things that stay with me:

1) Mum refused to take her pain medication. She sincerely believed she would die faster and constantly sleep if she took it. She had a very bad night where she was in pain and her heart was racing, Dad called the palliative care service in the morning and they said Mum should be admitted and then they would see if they could get her back home. She was happy to go in because

she was concerned about her heart. She let me give her oral painkillers then and was placed on morphine when admitted. If Dad, my brother or I had been able to explain that painkillers would not make her die faster, maybe she would have been more comfortable.

2) Sitting with Mum and Dad and completing her advance care directive one and a half weeks before she died. Let me make it clear, Mum was relatively young, she didn't want to die, and she wanted to meet her first grandchild. So, sitting with her and completing all the questions in the directive was probably the hardest thing I've ever had to do. There needs to be more support for the family and for the person who is dying when they are completing this at the end of their life. Luckily my friend who was studying nursing had planted the seed that this would need to happen; even so, it was incredibly difficult.

The dying stage was apparent once Mum was admitted to the palliative care hospital. The doctor who was overseeing her management explained what would happen to her, how she would most likely die. She didn't want to hear this and it made her quite upset. Her main concern was not being able to talk – how would she communicate? And this happened on day 3. It was at this point that my dad, brother and I began to keep vigil by her side – with the support of my sister-in-law, husband and extended family. We took turns sitting with her and holding her hand, day and night for five days. As I've said, she was scared and didn't want to be alone.

One of the best experiences and something that still stays with me to this day is the kindness, compassion and truly holistic care we experienced from another palliative care physician looking after her in her final days. He truly saw Mum, he saw us, he was present and talked about things that no health professional had spoken to us about – life and death, spirit and the unknown. Addressing questions like 'Why has this happened?' We don't know. He said how sad he was and that he would light a candle for Mum. He gave my dad a very big hug and told us to keep talking to her, to hold her hand and that she could still hear us.

My brother, cousin and I were present when Mum died. Dad had stepped out to pay for parking for another day and my husband went to find him. We were all tired and, as you will know if you have been through something similar, at the same time relieved she was no longer suffering. We sat with her a while and then packed up and left. In retrospect, I think I would have liked to sit there a little longer, but I felt like she had already left.

Take a look at the picture on page 22. It is what the map of my mum's journey looked like. The asterisks indicate the points at which receiving more information and support would have helped Mum and us, as primary carers, to have a better experience.

Bereavement felt less lonely. We had lots of support and people around us. Having a very large extended family, the next week involved a lot of organising and getting ready for the funeral. The funeral was very expensive, and I wish I'd known about funeral alternatives, DIY coffins and options with urns. I think there are some wonderful community and family-focused alternatives which also support the grieving process.

There is a clear distinction between pain and suffering. Medical professionals are generally very good at pain management. What I believe we are not so good at, as a sector and a community, is relieving people's suffering. I personally think that's because when we look at holistic health, we focus more on the body, a little on the mind but very little on the spirit. The best healthcare professionals I know pause to give support. They take the time to see their patients. They ask them how they are while really focusing on them, not while multi-tasking. They stop and look at their patients, their body language and their expression, listen to their tone and ask them what is going well and what they are worried about. We all have the ability to provide holistic care that also focuses on the mind and spirit, not just the physical. It's critical to continue exploring the important topic of person-centred care for older people.

I encourage anyone reading this book to increase your awareness about end-of-life issues within your community, engage with users of healthcare services and adopt some of the excellent initiatives that are occurring in the sector. Together, we can make a difference.

What do you think?

- What would be some rituals or symbols you would like to incorporate in your dying process or that of someone you love?
- Try building a list or a map of your family members and friends who could offer support to help you navigate the health system and the dying journey for you or one of your loved ones when the time comes.

Pre-diagnosis
Active, social
Travel
Cooking
Doctor: *EoL plan*
Zumba
Fun
Spanish class
Persistent cough and reflux
Shadows in lungs 2013
Lost weight and told to eat more protein
Steroids
Still socially active
Declined lung biopsy
Bad reflux
Juice diet – lost more weight
Early 2016 agreed to lung biopsy
Told it's not cancer and can be managed with medication

Diagnosis
Diagnosed idiopathic pulmonary fibrosis (lung disease – unknown reason)
Doctor: *explain disease progression, what to expect, and how to support*
Medication to stop spread available in India and US. Tried but didn't tolerate. Mum very fragile, less active
April 2016 told she has a year at best. Mum smiled and said 'I'm not allowed to fall over and die right now'
Dad primary carer
Doctor: *provide support to mum and family*
I went to every specialist appointment with mum & dad
Lung foundation peer phone support provided support for mum and dad
Less social and active
Looked forward to my wedding in August 2016 – gave her something to focus on
August difficulties in walking > fatigue and shortness of breath
Lung transplant not given due to frailty + age
Not eligible for my Aged Care (<65 years)
Sept
September admitted to hospital, not feeling good
After 1.5 weeks we still didn't know mum's prognosis or understand what was happening. We were anxious and frustrated.
Doctor: *advocate*

Palliative care
Cousin who's a GP told us we can request family meeting at hospital. Treating doctor to attend. He said 'I'm not good at this sort of thing. Mum is dying. Nothing they can do.'
Had started palliative care but not informed us. Anti-anxiety medications.
Doctor: *advocate*
Specialist referred to St Vincent's palliative care for in-home care.
Pal care difficult to access for cancer patients, health + support services difficult to navigate
Doctor: *provide support with coordination of care*
Clinical + practical care good, social/emotional support lacking
Doctor: *provide company for mum*
Mum was lonely and slept a lot
Organised, wheelchair, hospital bed, food tray
Learnt on the fly how to move mum, what to feed her, sponge bath/hygiene
Doctor: support us in learning how to manage mum at home
Worked from Brisbane & home. Supported mum with massage, aromatherapy, going outside
Created affirmations with mum for mental strength ('I am strong, I am able, I am calm')
Aim to ensure mum is in a peaceful environment. Found meditations/hymns for mum and dad to listen to. Mum slept.
Doctor: *provide an ear and spiritual support*
She didn't understand why this has happened to her. Had a lot of questions. Was looking for something she had done wrong & wondered if it was karma. She didn't want to die and had hope until the end.
Very difficult to lose independence – mum felt she was a burden
Doctor: *discuss funeral planning and options for what mum wants*
Holding on to see first grandchild, not eating much
Managed to take her to Gold Coast for birthday weekend. Special and very emotional. Always put on a brave face and smiled
My brother and I managed visitors, said to stop with stories of miracle cures
Refused to take ordine (thought it would make her die faster and didn't like not being lucid)
Hardest part was completing mum's advanced care directive. Not enough support for me or her. She said it would have been better to do it in 2 stages
Doctor: *provide support to me, mum, and dad in completing ACD*
Created keepsakes (handprints and finger painting) day before hospital admission

Dying
Doctor: *could have been on call to come home for support and call palliative care team earlier*
Had bad night, anxious and not sleeping. Too much for dad. Agreed to take ordine. St Vincent's organised to come pick up mum and treat symptoms + pain, then see if she can go home
Admitted, treating doctor told her most likely process for how she would die. She didn't want to know. I stayed with her that night.
Ate half weetbix. Tried to encourage her to eat more. Last meal.
Doctor: *could have given option of taking mum home & what we needed to do to support her.*
Scared she wouldn't be able to communicate. Couldn't speak from Wednesday. Closed her eyes. Doctor was incredibly kind, talked about why – we don't know. He lit a candle for mum.
5.5 days vigil in hospital – my brother, dad, and me
Doctor: *help manage family advice*
Photos, hymns, affirmations, massage
Active dying
No food/water for 3.5 days. Waiting and sitting was hard.
Family came every day to speak to mum.
Difficult to manage all visitors.
Doctor: provide emotional support
Created a room full of love
Mum died 7/11/2016 morning. My brother was holding her hand and I was there. Dad stepped out to walk with my husband and cousin.
Packed up and moved home. All family came over. Surreal feeling. Organised prayers and funeral.

Funeral
First week busy with funeral prep (photo montage, speech). We went with a big funeral/cremation package because we didn't know our options.
Washed and dressed mum's body with aunties, cousins, sisters. I knew she was gone.
Funeral was nice but surreal, feeling of it being strange. Would have done a few things differently in retrospect.
Bereavement and ongoing grief + learning to live normally was difficult
Rituals were important

A map of Mum's dying journey: the many asterisks indicate the points at which we would have been helped by more information. (A scaled-up, more readable version of this map can be found at: www.hammersmithbooks.co.uk/product/when-the-time-comes/)

5

The belated conversation and the imprecise directive

Young Ingrid married a neglectful, aggressive man and a few years later had to escape his grip and leave the country with their daughter to live in the US where her niece was working. Coming from humble beginnings, she had endured social alienation and financial hardship growing up. She had had only limited education so was intermittently unemployed over the years, but her hard work, sense of duty, self-built social networks, unconditional family support, creativity, love for her offspring and resilience pulled her through. After years of doing odd jobs to maintain a sufficient income, Ingrid started a new de-facto relationship and managed to buy a home on her own. However, her daughter then went astray and left Ingrid to raise and educate two grandchildren, which she did with passion and commitment.

While going through this major lifestyle change taking on her grandchildren, she suffered significant trauma when her younger sister, who was also her best-friend, babysitter and shopping buddy, was diagnosed with late-stage endometrial cancer. Despite trying conventional and multiple alternative therapies, her little sister died in hospital within six months of diagnosis, undergoing intrusive procedures that prolonged her suffering for no better result. Ingrid found that unbearable.

Ingrid finally decided it was time to consider retirement and enjoy the fruit of her efforts of 40 years. Instead, at the age 68 of in her pre-retirement year, she too was diagnosed with metastatic endometrial cancer. For around two years prior to the diagnosis becoming clear, she had been through the rigmarole of specialist consultations, tests, painful and costly procedures and hospitalisations with a mix of undefined symptoms and misdiagnoses. After confirmation of cancer, a few months after her sister's death, Ingrid submitted to every orthodox treatment offered, however aggressive, painful or undignifying, to ensure she stayed alive for the sake of the two teenage grandchildren she was raising.

However, several months later, and despite enduring radical surgery, chemotherapy and systemic and localised radiotherapy in rapid succession, she was told her cancer was not responding to treatment. She had intermittently lost and gained weight, lost and regrown her hair, lost and entertained hope.

Four months after her terminal diagnosis Ingrid started experiencing uncontrollable pain in her abdomen and spine. She presented at emergency several times, mostly to be sent home after a couple of days, but twice she was admitted to hospital to undergo more surgical procedures whose benefit she did not necessarily understand. However, she accepted the doctor's decisions on her behalf because of her lack of knowledge and complete trust in doctors' recommendations. The grandchildren were looked after by her de facto partner and sisters-in-law and were only able to see her rarely between school and after-school sporting activities. They got used to grandma being chronically ill and away and while they missed her dearly they also knew she was too sick to take care of them. The boys visited her several times a week after school and did their homework in the hospital room. It was the only way to be near her, regardless of whether she was asleep or under the influence of sedatives. They wanted her to be proud of their good behaviour and were praying she would live to see them graduate.

Every time she was admitted to hospital her grandchildren, partner and sisters-in-law suspected she would not come out alive, but Ingrid always felt if they offered hospital admission it was because there was a chance of recovery. Or was there? She had not lost hope nor had she understood or digested the meaning of words like 'metastasis' or 'palliative therapies'.

The family saw the progressive deterioration and suspected the truth about her prognosis being ominous and her death potentially imminent but this had never been disclosed by the treating team. Her sisters-in-law wanted the doctors to speak up. Instead, the clinicians persisted in administering drugs and surgical interventions but failed to honestly communicate the real devastating news to her or her family; they did not empathically attend to their emotional needs either. Once they prescribed morphine, Ingrid and her family understood she had reached the point of no return. It was an implicit disclosure but all the responsibility of understanding was left to the patient and her family.

During her last hospitalisation Ingrid had lucid days when she had constant visits by her extended family, who tried to comfort her and make her laugh, praised her, thanked her for her generosity and lovely disposition. She was overwhelmed with joy when they brought babies and pets to give her a sense of normality. She always asked for the babies to visit her again. She enjoyed the pampering one of her sisters-in-law gave her with manicures and hair grooming, and generally experienced a positive atmosphere to eclipse the unspoken sombre prognosis. Other days, in extreme discomfort, physically weak and despondent, she expressed her desire to give up. The health system was telling her to keep trying treatments, but eventually her body was telling her she'd had enough.

There had to be another way. She knew she had tried everything that had a scientific basis and was not prepared to go for untested alternative treatments like her sister. With a bit of tactfulness and loving caution, the women in her family suggested she arrange her legal Will to ensure the grandchildren's future financial stability, and an advance care directive to protect her own wellbeing. She did both while in hospital.

In the last few weeks she had a clear mind about what treatments she wanted and what others she was prepared to forego. She opted for home-based comfort care with 24-hour nursing support. The program involved her going home for two weeks and then to a hospice for her final days. 'A "hospice" is where you go when doctors have given up on you,' she replied. Somehow clinicians could not make her understand that highly qualified palliative care staff could provide the pain control and symptom relief she would eventually need, which could not be provided effectively at home. The family tried to persuade her, to no avail because she feared being abandoned. She just did not want to die in an institution as her sister had; and the uncertainty about what her trajectory to death would look like or how long it would last did not deter her from her decision to remain at home till the end.

Thanksgiving came, and the family wanted to share a last occasion with her even though Ingrid was semi-conscious for most of the day, on parenteral nutrition, intravenous hydration and a permanent oxygen mask. The family convened in her bedroom and thanked Ingrid for her loving and productive life, for working hard to raise the two boys, for her courage. They hoped she was 'there', understanding this was probably – most certainly – a farewell. They moved to the dining room to share the traditional meal while the nurse stayed in the room providing basic care to Ingrid. The atmosphere was sombre; they could hardly enjoy the food as some could not swallow while choking on their tears. Ingrid had always been a solicitous hostess and an amazing cook, and above all the glue that kept together her immediate family of three men: her partner, and the two boys. They all knew now there would be no Christmas together, they would no longer hear Ingrid's laughter.

Ingrid had insisted on staying at home to die but she suffered unmentionable bone pain even with the strongest analgesics and heavy sedation that could be administered at home. She never made it to the hospice. She died three weeks short of Christmas. Yet she preserved her autonomy to attain dignity and wellbeing because she still could. Unfortunately, the advance care directive she formulated for herself was based mainly on a personal preference to remain at home that ignored expert advice to receive comfort care at the hospice. Those expressed and written wishes kept her at home going through potentially preventable suffering that was as unbearable to her as it was to her family who heard her cry in pain every night. Advance care directives should embrace both personal values and scientific knowledge. Accepting objective expert advice about a different place of care does not take away a patient's control of their own situation. Ingrid chose not to take that advice because she misunderstood the role of the hospice.

Up to then, some of the family members had been estranged from each other, but no longer. Ingrid had reunited them without saying a word. She did not live to enjoy retirement or to see her grandchildren graduate, but given the role-model she was to them, and her legacy of self-determination, those children will certainly succeed.

What do you think?

- What do you think should be the balance between personal values and preferences and scientific knowledge when it comes to deciding where and how you receive treatments near the end of life?
- What is your understanding of the care provided in hospices? Why do you think the woman in this story wanted to avoid them?
- Have you thought if you would like to die in a hospice and why?

6

Not coming home

Helen was a loving wife, mother and grandmother of eight. Raised and living on a dairy farm, she knew what hard work was. Despite the endless droughts and coming close to losing the family cattle station, Helen's passion and determination not only to survive but also to thrive on an outback farm had paid off. At the age of 79 she felt accomplished, but today, far away from the fresh air of the countryside, she lay on a hard bed with a thin mattress in a major city hospital, in the middle of a chilly autumn. She had been transferred from a small medical clinic in her home town as she needed a higher level of care by a team of specialists in an acute care setting. She appeared frail and tired, wrapped in a white gown with tangled cords connected to her body coming from machines that were beeping every minute.

I had met Helen for the first time nearly 12 months before, when she had presented to the hospital for treatment of her chronic, irreversible lung condition. She and I had become very close during this time as she was with us for several days. Living in the country, five hours' drive from a large city, with the closest neighbour located a few kilometres away from his farm, Helen's husband Henry was always by her side while their eldest son managed the cattle station back home.

Up until the last couple of years, Helen had been leading a very active life on the farm despite periodic asthma attacks and a recalcitrant cough that had bothered her for years, mostly in winter. Sometimes she had ended up in hospital for a few days until the doctors were able to stabilise her. Although she was now not doing the physically demanding farm work she had been used to in her younger years, she had remained active and her mind sharp. She volunteered at the local school as a teachers' aid and spent most of her time with her grandkids on the farm, reading them books, baking and sewing for them. Helen would often say that the farm was her 'happy place'.

The first time I had met Helen she had told me that she often felt tired and her shortness of breath stopped her from doing many of the physical activities she had once enjoyed. She was becoming far more dependent on her husband for help around the house. She had confided to me that she was also struggling to look after the grandchildren. She found it increasingly difficult to pick up the young ones, and was lacking the energy to explore with them around the farm and show them the vegetable garden, the flower beds and the animals that would be theirs in the future.

Henry adored his wife, and as Helen had grown more fatigued, he had taken to bringing her breakfast in bed and taken over more chores around the house in addition to his farm work. When family asked if he needed any help at home he had always declined. Whether he was unaware of the growing burden, ashamed or embarrassed, I do not know. Looking back and after meeting the loving couple again, I wondered if Henry had been struggling at home, but somehow I never asked them, and I don't know if anybody else did in hospital. I also wonder now if that repeat hospitalisation would have been a good time for the treating specialist to broach the subject of prognosis, but after nearly two weeks in hospital and rehabilitation, Helen was medically cleared and safe for discharge.

I did not see Helen again until a few months later, when she was readmitted onto the geriatrics ward in the winter. She had a respiratory infection which was not responding to oral antibiotics at home and which had become more complicated by the presence of other underlying chronic illnesses. Her local doctor of many years recommended she attend the city hospital again. Prior to Helen arriving onto my ward, she had been placed on breathing devices, fluid resuscitation and regular nebulisers in the emergency department. I did not recognise her when I first saw her: she had lost a massive amount of weight, looked many years older and was often drowsy and sleepy during the day. I read on her medical record that she had been admitted to hospital again for two days just a few weeks earlier with similar symptoms. Nursing staff had to take care of most of her basic needs. Henry was with her daily at the hospital, would sit by her bed all day during visiting hours and often fed her and helped with bathing. He looked exhausted but, again, did not disclose he was unable to cope at home with his wife. He was very keen to get her back home and I often hoped for his sake that Helen would recover back to baseline. However, as days went by, this time there was no improvement in her condition.

Helen said to me one evening shift after visiting hours had finished that she 'wanted to go'. I remember feeling very saddened by this and when I questioned her further about why she had said this she told me how tired she was. I wanted to stay with her that evening to try and cheer her up and I knew she was appreciative of my efforts yet she would say in a motherly way, 'You are too young to understand how tired one can be.'

I do not believe Henry had ever been told that these repeat hospitalisations where his wife gradually deteriorated after each discharge were a sign that she was on the dying trajectory. Every shift I had that week I made sure I was allocated to Helen's room. I knew her dying journey had started but wanted her so badly to get better, not only for her sake but for Henry's too as he often said that if Helen was not home with him on the farm he would not know what to do with himself. I guess this would have been another perfect time to explain to him that she had passed the point of no return, but it was not my role to do that, nor that of the medical student helping us. And if the specialists whose role it was had already mentioned it to Henry, the news did not appear to have sunk in.

Helen's condition began to deteriorate quickly over the following days. Henry sat patiently in the room for long hours stroking her head and her hand, looking up in anticipation when any clinician walked past as if waiting for good news each day, wishing for confirmation that Helen would soon be up on her feet and coming home. I overheard him speaking to her and telling other staff that when she was able to come home he would organise help for the two of them. I felt he possibly believed that if he accepted help from their town's aged-care services, Helen could come back with him sooner. This was not the case, however, as she was too unwell to leave the ward.

This admission was unlike any previous one. Helen probably sensed this because after a few days she had undergone assessment by the intensive care team, plus chest X-rays, and IV fluids and oxygen were running at all times. All of these were new to her. Henry, however, continued querying us about why Helen was not getting better, although staff had explained repeatedly that she had a serious infection which was not easy to control given the chronic illness affecting her lungs. Looking back I do not know if Henry truly understood Helen's condition, but nobody seemed to go a step further in detailing the potential outcome in light of the lack of response to treatment. It was not a conspiracy of silence, just the clinical inertia of giving the treatments doctors are trained to deliver, or perhaps fear of taking Henry's last bit of hope away. In either case, Henry was none the wiser.

One evening shift I was with Helen and her condition was deteriorating further. She was now not talking in sentences and was becoming very drowsy, her eyes closed most of the time I was with her. Higher oxygen was given, medications were changed and drips of all sorts were again connected. She was too weak to eat and Henry was becoming very distressed at this. He could not understand why she was not hungry. Despite reassurance that she was indeed not feeling hungry, I had found him force-feeding her once, begging her to accept food while shedding silent tears. Of course I understood that Henry was doing this out of love and wasn't able to accept at this point that Helen's body was shutting down.

An emergency medical call was placed during the night when Henry had stayed. When the junior doctor arrived on the ward it was evident to nursing staff and the doctor that Helen was actively dying. Henry became very distressed and agitated to hear there was nothing more that could be done from a medical point of view. However, after discussion that night, it was decided to continue with medications until Helen's specialist could review and organise a meeting with Henry in the morning. Neither the nurses nor the medical student were in a position to have definitive words with Henry, as informing the patient's husband was – and is – the specialist's role.

I came back to work after two days and Helen was still on my ward. Henry told me that he had had a meeting with her doctor who had explained her condition and it was decided that she would be made as comfortable as possible while the condition ran its course. Henry was teary and withdrawn throughout my whole shift. He was becoming increasingly frustrated at the doctors and could not understand why Helen was not recovering from this lung infection. 'It was just two weeks ago, after her other hospitalisation, we were sitting at the farm having cups of tea and laughing as we remembered stories of the kids. Why was this cough any different?' he kept asking. 'Helen never told me that this cough was any more serious than the last. She has been sick many times this last year for the same reason and she has always come home.' He was also very distressed that Helen might be in pain as her breathing had changed, but she was unable to talk so, 'How would anyone know?' he would often say.

He did not know how she could be dying. This dying trajectory, with repeat hospital admissions, had been long and, while commonly witnessed by clinicians, was unrecognised by the husband. I am unsure if the clinicians managing her in previous admissions had mentioned to him the inevitable progression, but I was painfully aware of the looming prognosis that he could not yet grasp, two days after being told of the imminent outcome.

Henry had only a very short time to come to grips with Helen's condition and the devastating news that all active treatments would be suspended. The doctors had looked him in the eye and reassured him that she would not suffer, they had been honest with him about the irreversibility of it all and made sure he did not have false hope for a miracle; they gave him time to absorb the shocking reality and offered to answer any questions about the dying process, but Henry had no questions. He slowly swallowed his tears and accepted the fact that Helen was not coming home. Not this time. Not ever.

He stayed with Helen during my shift, kissing her forehead and whispering to her ear, probably nice memories of their many years together, or about how the garden would keep her memory alive, or how he would make her proud with his baking for the grandkids in her absence. I could not hear but could sense Helen peacefully letting go. She died with Henry next to her that afternoon. All staff had gathered around to support Henry and Helen as they had both warmed our hearts with their evident love for each other through good and hard times.

What do you think?

- Sometimes, as in this case, it is the carer who needs to know when to get ready to let go. Whose job do you think it was to tell Henry and at what point? How could the clinicians have done this better?
- Clinical inertia means that clinicians do what they are trained to deliver: treatments. At what times do you think they should perhaps step back if the treatment is not beneficial and communicate this so families can move from hope to acceptance?

7

Letting go of love and life

I am about to hang up when after what feels like several minutes of ringing, a woman answers.

'Hello? Hello?' Her voice sounds breathless, as though she has rushed for the phone. I can tell just from those two words she has uttered that she is a woman in her twilight years... 70s, maybe 80s. I feel guilty that she has had cause to run.

I say hello quickly and explain I am a research nurse from the hospital and that I would like to speak to her husband so that I can follow up on his health. He had responded to a research interview late last year during hospitalisation and never returned to hospital; we have not heard from him.

'I'm sorry, dear,' she says, matter-of-fact but almost wearily too, 'He died a few months ago.'

My hospital had no notification of his death at another institution; I feel inappropriate, offer her my condolences and tell her I am sorry for her loss. She reassures me and thanks me. She tells me 'her Ernie' had a long battle and the end was a relief; she knew he wouldn't suffer any more. Even so, I venture, it must be difficult to experience such a loss.

'Yes,' she says, 'I have lost my best friend but he was in so much pain at the end that I would never wish him to still be alive.'

I say that must have been very difficult for her.

'Yes, it was,' she says, but goes on to tell me that she and her husband, Ernie, had had a good life and been very fortunate. Blessed with three sons, they had had a happy marriage. She tells me when Ernie got sick, her sons and their wives rallied round to help out where they could. Small things like mowing the lawn and so forth. Ernie started to decline quite rapidly just before Christmas. He was admitted to another hospital near their home with a serious infection and along with everything else it seemed unlikely that he would return home.

The palliative care team came and spoke with her. Did she want Ernie to be resuscitated in the event of a cardiac arrest? Her voice is beginning to crack a little as she recounts her decision-making process. I can tell she is crying. She explains how much pain and discomfort Ernie had been in for several months; the multiple tablets he was on offering little to no relief; how he became more dependent on her; and how his mobility and general ability to do anything for himself had significantly declined in the last couple of months.

'It must have been very difficult for you,' I say.

'Well, yes,' she concedes, 'But I didn't mind. I loved him so and would have done anything for him.'

She sobbed audibly then, the cry catching in her throat. Tears form in my own eyes. The grief of this woman and her love for her husband, her best friend, are palpable, even over the telephone. I tell her Ernie was a very lucky man to have had such a caring and committed wife. She thanks me for saying so. Then I tell her:

'You made the right decision in stopping him from suffering unnecessarily.'

She agrees in a whisper. I say:

'It was an act of love to let him go, and he would have wanted that for sure.' She gives a sigh of relief.

'I think so, I hope so.'

It shows courage and knowing each other well to be able to represent a loved one's last wishes, whether or not they are in writing. In my experience, not every patient has that privilege. She goes on to tell me that Ernie's care was assumed by palliative care a few days after Christmas. He died on December 30. His death was peaceful and painless, precipitated by four-hourly shots of morphine. He was surrounded by his family and wife. She tells me the nurses and doctors were amazing – very caring and compassionate. She couldn't fault the care he received in the end, even if there was never an end-of-life conversation or an advance care directive before that hospital admission. The question must have come as a shock, but she knew Ernie well enough to allow the palliative care team to offer him comfort rather than resuscitation.

I ask her how she feels now, how she is coping with her loss and whether she feels supported by her family. She tells me she is coping okay, that her boys and their families have been wonderful and check in on her constantly. She misses Ernie terribly and often feels teary but also feels reassured and takes solace in the knowledge that he is not suffering anymore. I reiterate her observation and thank her for taking the time to speak with me and share her story; I tell her I appreciate how difficult it is to talk of loss and grief.

She thanks me also for calling, for listening to her, and tells me it has been of some comfort to talk about him. She wishes me well with my research and hangs up.

What do you think?

- Some people nominate another person they trust to make treatment decisions on their behalf if they lose capacity. How would you prepare to feel capable of representing a loved one's wishes (such as 'Do not resuscitate') if they are unable to decide for themselves because they are permanently unconscious or suffer from advanced dementia or catastrophic stroke?
- What sort of things do you think would reassure a person that they made the right treatment decision on behalf of a loved one who died?

8

The 'daughter from California' syndrome

Amelia was a funny former school principal who, after 30 years of retirement, still had a teacher's cane in her bedroom to remember the good old times when corporal punishment of schoolchildren was not considered a crime. At 85 years old she still drove like a hoon and swore like a teenager. She was a frail woman with a history of smoking and bleeding stomach ulcers, and had suffered from diabetes for 25 years and hypertension for a decade. She sort-of-kept those illnesses at bay with a collection of tablets in her Webster packs, but drank wine every day and surreptitiously had daily sugary treats she shared with her grandchildren when other adults weren't looking.

Amelia had also gone through two hip replacements, multiple falls at home and prolonged hospitalisations – the story of many elderly citizens. She lived in her own home near the beach with her husband and enjoyed feeding the lorikeets on her balcony, working on projects around the kitchen and the garden, and painting with oils in the back room. For the past few years she had been the primary carer of her husband, who suffered from advanced dementia. She showered, dressed, combed, fed him and protected him from accidental harm, and in addition she cleaned, cooked, shopped for groceries and paid the bills.

Hers was the only name he remembered and the last familiar face he recognised. With the help of hired community carers and some family members who took turns to visit weekly, Amelia managed to get some respite so she could also keep in touch with former colleagues from her earlier days. She periodically drove several hours to get to a rural area where she had worked as a young teacher to join the annual gatherings. She led a very active life, physically and intellectually.

Most of her children visited regularly, took took her and their father on outings and celebrated family occasions together – that is, all except for *'the daughter from California'*[3], the eldest child, who had been estranged from her parents as a teenager and from her siblings for most of her adulthood. She lived a post-modernist life in a rural area in the same state as the parents but hundreds of kilometres away, and only contacted them occasionally. She visited their home once a year and stayed for a week, a time of great stress for the elderly couple as the daughter tried to make up for lost time by re-organising their home, cleaning obsessively and generally upsetting their well-established, slow-paced, frugal lifestyle. She put them through a marathon of appointments with service providers, confronted the system's incompetence with threatening phone calls and intrusive letters on behalf of the parents but without their consent. She even secretly contacted the traffic authority to cancel her mother's driving licence 'to protect her from harm' but failed to arrange alternative transport for her mother's errands, effectively sentencing Amelia to home detention and making her totally dependent on others. Then she would leave the elderly couple exhausted before she disappeared for another year feeling very pleased with herself for having done *'the right thing'.*

The siblings were extremely irritated by this selfish behaviour because they had to pick up the pieces of broken relationships with healthcare staff and social service providers, and be in charge of all the errands and the driving and other chores the mother could no longer do.

When Amelia needed another hip replacement as she was in constant pain, which limited her in doing her chores, the children arranged for a couple of weeks of respite for their father/her husband so she could take time to have the procedure and recover. During surgery, however, there was a medical misadventure due to her brittle bones, and the operation became lengthy and complicated, resulting in an unplanned prolonged hospital stay of a couple of months and a serious hospital-acquired infection. During that protracted hospitalisation she lost 20 kg and was hardly recognisable at discharge. She was never the same again. She could not go out of the house without assistance and yet would not consider living anywhere else but at home.

For her husband, the two-week respite care became two months and he was not coping well with the unfamiliar environment and routine. He appeared confused and distant. The *'daughter from California'* did not show up all this time. Amelia became depressed at the realisation that caring for her husband was no longer possible while she had to recover herself, and this was going to take several months. The children who lived nearby and visited often saw the gradually increasing frailty and deterioration and suggested the elderly couple should no longer live a dangerous life in their home but should move to a supervised facility. They also prompted their mother to arrange a legal Will and advance care directive. Amelia got on with the former but ignored the latter. Dying was not part of her plan.

Her plan was to make sure her husband was cared for with dignity at home until his death and then she would consider looking after herself. However, eventually and reluctantly she agreed to move into a facility where she could live semi-independently and visit her husband daily in the high-dependency ward. A nursing home was chosen jointly by Amelia and her closest children.

It was sad to see her leaving the place where she had spent so many years with her husband, losing her ability to care for the garden, and having to choose which memories to pack in boxes for the move and which ones to discard, knowing that many of them would not fit in her single nursing home unit. Most of her children helped with packing, cleaning and relocating them to the new aged-care facility, and continued to visit them weekly.

The *'daughter from California'* did not get involved in the packing or moving but this did not stop her guilt-driven obnoxious behaviour. On some level she felt left out by living far away and not getting on with her siblings. On another level, given the impending decline of both parents, she had to make up for all the years she had not been helping or accompanying them, not doing her daughterly duty. Unfortunately, her belated approach was counterproductive. She would call the nursing home periodically to harass the staff for not doing enough, and complained to government officials about the 'deplorable state' of the facility which she hardly ever visited. Even though she was not a healthcare professional, she insisted her demented father undergo major surgery for a newly discovered cancer when the medical team had already consulted the immediate family and agreed on the recommendation for conservative and less risky oral treatment. Again, common sense prevailed and the father was treated with the least harmful medicines rather than with surgery. The nursing home staff were incredibly patient and tolerant. They could have terminated the residential contract with the family to prevent further inconvenience and distress, but they stood their ground as they had the residents' best interests at heart. They protected the couple's well-being by introducing new visiting and calling rules and testifying in court about what was best for both Amelia and her husband.

After eight months of physical rehabilitation in the nursing home, Amelia's fracture had healed but she had made only one friend in that time at the facility and this friend died shortly after that. Amelia became withdrawn and sedentary despite having regular visits from most of her children. Her husband no longer recognised her and, in fact, rejected her when she visited one week. That unexpected development sent Amelia into a state of detachment from life and she shut down emotionally. She had been erased from her life-partner's memory. What else was there to live for?

A few days later she had chest pain but did not tell any of the nurses or relatives who rang her that weekend. It was only on the weekly medical check-up three days later that the doctor noticed she was too pale and weak and found her blood pressure to be too low. She concluded that Amelia had had a massive heart attack some time in the three days before and needed to be transferred to hospital emergency by ambulance. On arrival she was admitted to intensive care where doctors inserted a stent to alleviate the coronary blockage, but it was all too late and she went into acute, irreversible kidney and liver failure.

The family was contacted about not only the heart, but also many other organs irreparably failing, and the specialists told Amelia that she had 48 hours to live. She felt relieved that she now knew for sure she was going to die and was satisfied with her life achievements and her marriage of 60 years. She had an opportunity to say the face-to-face goodbyes to some of the children and grandchildren in hospital, including to her husband who was quickly brought to her hospital bed from the nursing home. Only the '*daughter from California*' did not turn up but managed to speak some last words to her on the phone.

By not communicating her heart attack symptoms, Amelia might have chosen to precipitate her exit from life without an explanation or an apology. She preserved that last bit of autonomy and dignity. She was ready to depart and still joking on the last day of her life and died peacefully under sedation within 24 hours of admission to intensive care.

A couple of months after Amelia's death the siblings had to go to court to stop the '*daughter from California*' from applying for guardianship to remove the demented father from his familiar environment – his new home. She intended to take him to a different facility near her. She thought of herself as the heroine sacrificing herself and saving the day, yet the confusion of a residential change and isolation from his usual companions would have been detrimental to the father's health. The courts ruled in favour of the father remaining at the originally chosen nursing home near the majority of his adult children.

The '*daughter from California*' continued giving a hard time to the rest of the family for months about the inheritance and then lost all contact with her siblings until a year later, the last time they met, when they bumped into each other at the father's funeral, organised by those who lived nearby and had visited him till the end.

What do you think?

- How much if anything do you know about laws in your country establishing a hierarchy of people who can be surrogate decision-makers for someone who has lost their capacity and has not made a power of attorney?
- What are your views about children living far away having the right to override a decision made by the live-in person in charge of the day-to-day care of an older patient?
- What do you think about respecting the autonomy of the dying elderly to not receive further treatment if they think this is in their best interest?

9

My 'new normal'

I've been married to my beautiful husband, Stretch, for a little over 45 years. When he was 58, I noticed he was occasionally having some hiccups with memory and procedures at work. I assumed that because he was in a very stressful job, his coming retirement at age 60 would relieve him of that stress and everything would be okay. However, by the time Stretch was 61 and had been retired for over a year, I realised that this wasn't just a hiccup but there was actually something causing him to forget things, become disoriented while driving, put things in strange places and generally have a growing difficulty performing routine functions of life. At the age of 63, a driving assessment resulted in his being given another six months before reassessment, even though I was convinced that he was no longer safe on the road; thankfully, he agreed to stop driving at the end of that year.

However, it wasn't until Stretch was a little over 64 years old that we finally got a definitive diagnosis of younger-onset Alzheimer's disease; we had to travel well out of our area to find a geriatrician who was able to pinpoint the cause of Stretch's by now seriously impaired functionality in even the simplest tasks of living. The diagnosis confirmed what I had suspected for three years already, so while it was confronting to have an actual diagnosis, it wasn't any longer a shock at that stage. I believe the shock came much earlier than that, when I faced the reality of the nightmare of seeing my strong, manly husband gradually become dependent on my management of our lives, and I realised that I wasn't going to wake up in the morning and find that everything was okay.

That became the first in a series of 'new normals' I had to adjust to over the years. I guess that's the pervading feeling that persists as the journey continues – I would love to wake up from the nightmare and have my sweetheart by my side, just as we once were.

In December of the same year, the reality of this awful disease hit home as Stretch almost overnight became aggressive, psychotic, depressed and agitated. Even though we both had a great aversion to drugs of any sort, medication helped Stretch to return to a more 'normal' demeanour. I was relieved that choosing to attempt pharmacological help made it possible for me to continue caring for Stretch, who by now was dependent on me for every aspect of life – yet another adjustment to my new reality.

The following year, I became increasingly more tired, as not only was I now caring for Stretch in almost every aspect of living, but he had begun wandering at night as well. A bit reluctantly but in bad need of some time to recharge my batteries, I took advantage of residential respite care for Stretch, for two weeks at a time on a couple of occasions. On admission at the first respite place, I was shocked to be asked to indicate what my instructions were if my relatively young husband had a life-threatening medical crisis while he was in the facility. I was totally unprepared for these questions, even though Stretch and I had often talked about this and agreed on no resuscitation, no gastric tube, etc: it was confronting! Not long after this, I found out this is called an advance care plan or directive and I went into the website and completed one for both of us.

The first respite facility he stayed at was not for him as he was terrified and felt locked up. I decided to attend a *'Going to Stay at Home'* course which was a wonderful help in educating us carers to see what aids were already in place to help with caring for someone as long as possible at home and also with giving us guidance on how to choose permanent residential accommodation and how to be an advocate for our loved one in care. The course entailed living for a week in a room which was exactly the same as those being occupied by permanent aged-care residents. This gave me my first experience of seeing what it 'looked like' to have Stretch living in care, and for me it gave an extremely important insight into how this could be much better than I had envisaged. My only knowledge up to that point had come from the earlier disastrous residential respite visit and from many visits to friends and relatives in multi-bedrooms where the lounge room was filled with wheelchairs and bed chairs, all positioned around a television and all occupied by staring or sleeping residents.

By the time the week of the '*Going to Stay at Home*' course was up, not only had I learned a great deal about what to look for in a nursing home, but I also felt very much relieved that not all aged care is the same. I had the opportunity to live what his new normal would be like. Stretch settled very comfortably into this new nursing home at night.

This second period in residential respite care resulted in staff indicating that Stretch needed to be in residential care permanently; he needed more in-depth care than I was equipped to safely give him. So he had to go from the respite facility into permanent care and I suffered the pain and shock of realising that he would never walk through our front door again ... and that pain doesn't go away even today, years on.

And so began this new journey, where I became Stretch's advocate in care. He seemed to feel safe and secure and there was no asking of when he was going home, except on rare occasions in the early months. Stretch doesn't have a room on his own and personally I believe that is a significant plus. There are always staff or residents or visitors in and out of his room, so when he is there, he's not left alone without personal interaction. With other facilities opening very close to our home over time, I have no intention of moving him, even though it would be more convenient for me: I have found him a home in which our 'new family' will walk compassionately with us through to the very end of this difficult journey.

Stretch is now 68 years old and has been in permanent residential care for two-and-a-half years. The advance care plan that his current nursing home holds has instructions for him not be placed in a room by himself and for him not to be moved to another facility. It's in writing, so that's all in place now. We've also discussed this with our family and, to be honest, it's a step I recommend for all families; you never know what lies around the corner and it's so important that your loved ones know your wishes so they can honour them in a time of crisis.

The early months of this year were momentous. Stretch had a fall in February which left him apparently unable to remember how to walk so he was in bed most of the time, or occasionally in a special bean chair, from which he couldn't fall. In April we had our Military Memorial service, in which I contributed by leading a prayer. What a special day for us! Stretch was presented with his Defence Force Medal for his service in the Army Reserve in the 1960s. To know that he wore this on what will probably be his last Remembrance Day was so wonderful.

Over the past three years I've learned a lot about this new and very important phase in my caring role and I continue to learn daily, as each new stage of the journey into 'my new normal' unfolds. A couple of months ago, Stretch resumed walking; his chew/swallow reflex no longer works, so his diet consists of soft food and drinks. He spends his day either walking the corridors or sleeping on the nearest unoccupied bed. I am aware as I watch him that he seems exhausted with the effort of functioning, even on this limited level, and so he needs to lie down and rest after only very short periods of walking. Walking means he is again at risk of another fall, because he's not all that steady, and I don't consider restraint appropriate.

He spends much of his time sleeping; when he's awake, he's generally alert and often 'looking' at something which only he can see. He acknowledges me as someone important, but has long since forgotten our marriage relationship. He sees our children, grandchildren and family members as familiar faces, but that's as far as it goes.

For the period Stretch was bedridden I was aware of another thing that he and I had lost: we had always walked holding hands, wherever we were. When he went into care, I would join him in his endless walking, around the corridors, holding hands. I'm very grateful that we can now do this again for a few minutes when I visit. How I hate this awful disease!

Being on this journey with Stretch in residential care has meant learning to grow comfortable with 'my new normal' – that's my life seeming to be painfully split in two: my life where I visit with Stretch and then there's my 'other life.' That's a challenging learning curve for a couple who have grown so deeply in love over 45 years: I'll never be completely adjusted to it, but as the months and years have passed, God has been my comfort in all that we've experienced. Yes, I get lonely and I miss Stretch terribly, but I'm never alone. I'm looking forward to that great day when he's whole again and we can walk together down the Golden streets. I hope you'll find it encouraging to join me along the way as I reflect on what I've learned while I continue to seek the best for the man I love.

What do you think?

- The wife in this story has been through several adaptation periods (new normals) over time. What has your experience of adaptation been like with your own health or that of a loved one?
- How long do you think it takes to adjust to a 'new normal'?

51

10

'Ready to go' Bob

Bob greeted me with a big toothy grin as I entered his hospital room in the emergency department. At 97 years of age, he still had a sparkle in his eyes. Despite not feeling his finest, he had an infectiously happy energy about him. He agreed readily to participate in my research survey, and enjoyed telling stories of his life.

Three years before, Bob had lost his wife. They had been married for 70 years, and she had made it to the impressive age of 90. He talked about her with a smile, but I could see his eyes becoming teary. Now 97, Bob said, with that same grin on his face, that he would be happy not to wake up in the morning.

'No-one else is left,' he said.

He spoke of some young people from the church who visited him every Saturday, a young couple who recently invited him to their wedding, his two sons, 12 grandchildren and 13 great-grandchildren. There was still a lot of vibrancy in Bob's life, but he was the last of his generation and he was ready to go. His greatest fear was that he would end up too weak to keep caring for himself at the home he'd shared with his wife. He had no doubt that he would rather die than be sent to a nursing home.

Often, when people say that they're ready to go, the news is received with a chorus of 'Oh, you're okay,' 'Chin up,' or 'You've got plenty of years in you yet,' but I was impressed with the smiling, matter-of-fact way in which Bob said it. He really meant it.

After Bob had left the emergency department to be admitted to the ward, I realised that there had not been an NFR (not-for-resuscitation) order in his notes. Despite his open willingness to discuss his wishes, his readiness to die, this had not been committed to writing. I doubt Bob was aware of what would transpire if he happened to have a cardiac or respiratory arrest in hospital. Despite having told people that he was ready to go, without the correct legal documents, the medical personnel caring for him might be compelled to enact potentially lifesaving measures. CPR might break his frail ribs, a breathing tube would be inserted into his trachea, and he would be hooked up to drips and machines to keep his heart pumping.

Bob had been brought to hospital with a relatively minor affliction, so hopefully an arrest was unlikely. However, in my role as a nurse in a hierarchical system where doctors initiate these conversations, all I could do was hope that his medical team on the ward would be forward-thinking enough to discuss his true wishes and get them down on paper before it was too late (I am aware that other healthcare systems have different and expanded roles of practice for nurses).

I found out later that Bob had been discharged back home and managed well for a month before revisiting hospital after collapsing. He had suffered a minor heart attack. He recovered well and again was sent home to look after himself, this time with some supportive services to help him manage activities of daily living.

When the time comes, Bob's end of life could continue as it has been, having multiple admissions to hospital, and possibly dying during one of them, ... or progressively deconditioning after each hospitalisation, with increasingly less hope of returning to his previous strength, and each time a step closer to a nursing home for the final part of his life. This would be Bob's worst-case scenario, but for some people would be a preferred choice.

Chapter 10

There are other alternatives, including community care and finally hospice care. What is clear is that Bob has been '*ready to go*' for a while, but his body continues to endure the efforts of a health system determined to do all they can to keep him here.

What do you think?

- How do you feel about you or your older relative or friend spending the last months of life in and out of hospitals? What about avoiding the emergency department and being managed in a nursing home?
- Whose role do you think it is to raise the subject of 'no resuscitation'? What do you think about a patient proposing it when they are in control of their affairs?

11

What Dad learnt from Mum's death

My parents were about to retire and were living by themselves in a cold country in the Northern hemisphere while we – their three children – were all married and living elsewhere, enjoying warmer landscapes. When she was 60, my mother was diagnosed with an uncommon, slow-growing, secondary liver cancer and doctors couldn't identify the primary source. It came as a big shock to all of us as she had had vague symptoms for a long time and her condition had been misdiagnosed for many years before a liver CT scan confirmed the case.

Mum went stoically through various management plans she didn't necessarily understand, but she consented to undergo a string of treatments from conventional to experimental therapies, and my dad – her sole carer – used to give her massages, take her to appointments and feed her himself.

After five long years of battling this monster illness, the cancer became very aggressive and spread to her bones and spine. She was offered the option to participate in a clinical trial as a last resort. This gave my dad the hope and belief that this would suppress the tumour and put it into remission. He was not well informed because, unfortunately, this was not the case, but the clinicians did not make it clear to him that this was palliative management to buy her extra time with us.

Due to the progressive complications, Mum went into kidney and liver failure and retained fluids to the extent that her skin was leaking non-stop. She was a very strong fighter, still very optimistic at all stages. From deep down inside, I knew the end was approaching. All of us children – but not Dad – had a certainty it was coming. I believe even Mum suspected this, but we did not talk about it. She soldiered on without complaining while my dad was in complete denial, harbouring unwavering hope.

Mum's main fear was not death but CT scans and nuclear imaging as clinicians would struggle to find a non-ruptured vein to insert a needle into to inject the colouring contrast dye. Neither Dad nor the rest of the family discussed what mattered to her, such as her fear of needles or dread of being in hospital. There was no discussion whatsoever with her clinicians about palliative care, the end-of-life journey, or her wishes and the options of staying at home or being in hospital! On the contrary, people around her, including Dad, were encouraging Mum to travel abroad to visit family. To this day I don't know if our other relatives were also in denial or whether they felt they had a duty to do everything available to maintain hope, or if they really believed she could win that battle.

Christmas arrived in its white frozen dress; it was too cold and it was very hard to travel as most roads were blocked with snow – a difficult time to be caring for an ill person at home. When my mother became short of breath again, Dad panicked being alone with her, so he asked neighbours to come and help him carry her, as ambulance services were only responding to trauma cases affected by severe weather. Mum was gasping for air while the neighbours spent what seemed like a long time clearing the snow that was blocking the driveway to be able to carry her to the car on a wooden chair. On the way out, while being carried away, Mum asked the guys to put the chair on the ground and then to walk her slowly while she looked around her, absorbing everything: the neighbourhood, the place she had lived in for her entire life, finally enjoying the peaceful silence in the street. Her yearning look said it all: she wanted to be home, that warm and controlled environment which she had the feeling she would never come back to. In a way, in this brief journey to the garage, she was saying goodbye to the trees, her flower pots and the memories of her married life.

Again she went through the hectic emergency department, had tests done and a drip set up, and was transferred to a ward. The oncologist then came with a stern look and told Dad, 'Call your children. I'm afraid no further chemotherapy treatment will be offered as she no longer qualifies to continue her participation in the clinical trial.' Dad's knees were shaking as this was not the news he had expected in a safe place (the hospital). He felt exhausted and shocked, and in his despair he felt abandoned by the health system.

Despite the time difference between countries, he immediately rang me from the hospital, obviously distressed: 'I've been forced to leave Mum behind at the hospital and the oncologist has made a decision to stop treatment! I was not consulted about what I wanted or what the family thought of it,' he gasped. 'They just told me what is going to happen. How can they have robbed us of hope like this?'

I now confirmed that this was the beginning of the end for Mum, so I told my sisters and we all booked flights so we could be with her. Dad went home by himself to digest the news and prepare for the next chapter.

'We are ready to hear your news on how long our mum has to live if possible,' I wrote in my email to the doctor in charge of her care at the other end of the world.

'Is there anything else that we should know about her condition?' I asked.

No reply. I interpreted that silence as confirmation of my worst fears but didn't have time to feel betrayed by the healthcare system or abandoned by the doctors. My priority was to be with Mum.

Getting to Mum's side wasn't straightforward coming from different parts of the world and from different time zones; what's more, airports were closed due to snow storms. I decided to go straight from the airport to the hospital without stopping at Dad's house. I don't know how I did it but it was lucky I managed to get to the hospital and be with Mum before the next severe snowfall. I had to upgrade her hospital room to one where relatives were allowed to be with patients overnight.

Mum was very happy seeing me next to her; she kept asking me about the rest of the family and was very worried about their flights and travel plans. Unfortunately, both my sisters' flights were delayed. Eventually my eldest sister managed to be home with Dad, but neither could join us at the hospital due to heavy blizzards and road closures. After all those years of being married and looking after her, Dad missed out on being by Mum's side for the last two weeks of her life. I'm sure he regretted having returned home from the hospital before the storm started. He surely wished he could have been trapped in the hospital with Mum. For him and my sisters, being near Mum was only possible after 10 days, when roads were cleared and traffic got back to normal. Once there, one of my sisters stayed with me every day and we slept next to Mum every night for the entire hospitalisation.

Sadly, soon after we finally met as a family, we had to face all these questions which we were not prepared for – hard family decisions on whether we agreed on Mum having central-line dialysis through her skin into one of the large veins in her neck; whether we consented for her to have a feeding tube down her throat into her stomach. We had no idea how to decide.

Mum's condition was managed by several medical teams: oncology, cardiology, endocrine, urology and finally nutrition. One team after the other came to assess her and talked in medical jargon. We saw different faces every time, including those of trainees. Where was the '*integrated care*' when you needed it? We weren't even sure if they talked to each other. That was not what they call '*patient-centred communication*', for sure. Dad did not know which specialist was in charge of her medical decisions. We were confused, anxious, exhausted and wanting some honest and consistent advice.

Dad was not asking many questions or asking Mum for her views. We probably agreed to everything which Mum did not want! She did not want the thick plastic tube running through her neck, nor the nasal plastic tube dumping food in her stomach. This also applied to the urinary tube, cannula and morphine pump. She did not want to see new faces rolling her from one ward to the next, queuing with her at the lifts, waiting at the dialysis department for her turn. All she wanted was the touch from her kids and assurance that we would be okay, and to hear that we loved her. When she couldn't talk, she used to roll her eyes backwards trying to express her feelings about all the aggressive interventions she was enduring, as if saying 'Let me go.' But when she was able to talk, she used to say, 'I love you deeply, my dear family,' and she wouldn't take this time to complain or explicitly tell the doctors to stop.

For a few days Mum slept like an angel; she used to open her eyes, look at us and then fall asleep again.

On the 15th of January, the palliative care team informed us that none of the treatment options were helping and recommended that a better option was to give Mum the peace she wanted rather than all of these invasive interventions she was getting. Dad did not speak up even though the news devastated him. None of us had the knowledge or skills to disagree with specialist medical advice, no matter how much we wanted Mum to stay with us. It was a harrowing decision to cease active treatment, but we approved their recommendation. We assured her that we would be okay, including Dad... and I whispered in her ear, telling her how much I loved her and that if she needed to go it was okay to do so.

She finally stopped suffering. She left with the good memories of her house and the sight of her loving family by her side.

A year passed before Dad could discuss the experience. When he did, he did it all by himself, after long and hard consideration. He is no longer in denial about the need to discuss end-of-life sooner rather than later. He has learnt that there is an option to stop futile treatments earlier and allow people to die at home. He says if he had the opportunity to go through it again, he would have given Mum the chance of going for comfort care earlier to prevent unnecessary suffering. She could have spent the last 18 days of her life at home, wrapped in her own blankets, surrounded by family. Yes, Dad might have regrets for what happened to Mum, but with his new understanding, he now has told us what he wants for himself.

What do you think?

- Sometimes being in denial about a relative with poor prognosis helps the survivors or the dying person. Who do you think would benefit most and why?
- What aspects of treatment preferences would you speak about to your doctor after a serious diagnosis to prevent unnecessarily aggressive interventions?
- What do you want for yourself?

12

Too late to change her mind

How many people can say they've had friendships that lasted four decades? I'm one of those lucky ones.

At 65, 45 years after we first met, Lauren was the same skinny woman she had been at university – a not very funny, highly organised, matter-of-fact lady, very set in her ways, but very reliable and fiercely independent. When they were young, Lauren was very close to and best friends with her older sister, Frankie, who shared a love of dancing, and they did everything together while studying for the same career.

I had met them during my first year at university, when both came from their rural town to the large city where I lived. They had a plan to live together after completing the undergraduate course. We formed a study group and joined laboratory practices throughout those years until graduation. After that I moved away to establish myself, while they went together to a neighbouring country.

As she became successful really quickly, Lauren invested her savings in a house in our native country, which she rented out all year long, and hoped to go back to one day in her old age. We maintained a long-lasting friendship that would stretch into our golden years. Even when I was abroad, on one of her visits to our native country, Lauren visited my mum, who had recently had major cancer surgery.

Lauren and Frankie had both gotten married and started their own lives, yet within a few years of graduation Lauren divorced without bearing any children. She then went to live with her sister and they set up a joint business venture for which they travelled together again. In that time, Frankie had three children whose company Lauren enjoyed when they joined on some of the trips. Life was good, and they regularly travelled to the other side of the world and back. However, after about 20, years the country where they were living went into turmoil and a sudden change in government regime turned their lives upside down. The sisters parted ways and Lauren migrated again, this time to the country where I was living with my husband and kids. Now middle-aged, she and I were often in contact over many years, while her sister remained locked in the other country.

One day, years later, Lauren received a call that changed her life. Frankie gave her the devastating news that she, Frankie, had been diagnosed with terminal cervical cancer. Although they had been separated for years, Lauren rushed to Frankie's side to be with her older sister but did not tell me or anyone else. Frankie did not want to share her private hell beyond her immediate circle. It was a harrowing time for both sisters, going through the motions of multiple medical appointments, comforting each other about the prognosis, talking about Frankie's hair loss, helping her buy the wigs they tried out together, sharing childhood memories, and promising that nobody would find out about her illness, be it family or friends. About five months after the initial news, Lauren called to let me know about Frankie's passing. I was in shock, thinking she had had a heart attack because the news was so sudden. I had no idea she had been ill.

Following that intense period after Frankie's death, Lauren became depressed and expressed in our conversations that she wanted to be with her sister in eternity because she missed her terribly. I always reminded her of the nephews she had, and how important her support would be for them and for her 90-year-old mother, but she was never the same. I don't think she ever recovered.

After her sister's death, Lauren considered returning to our home country even though she wasn't of retirement age. However, since her work was where I lived and she had health insurance coverage here, she came back to plan for a future retirement date instead. This may have been her last opportunity to return to her homeland, but we didn't know that. The time immediately after Frankie's death was lonely and dark. To Lauren it seemed as if it were never-ending.

We remained in contact and I could hardly believe we had been friends for over four decades. We were both 65 years old when she finally retired, but she did not return to our homeland as planned. It's funny how goal-posts keep moving and we refuse to feel older or ready to start another chapter in our lives. I was and still am a busy mother and businesswoman with little time to go anywhere on holidays. By contrast, once retired Lauren loved to ride the subway and go places. She took pleasure in being very active, attending yoga, dance and computer classes, and participating in all the celebrations at the seniors' centre. Being indoors in her modest rented apartment in that industrialised country was not for her, especially because the landlady turned the air-conditioning off during the day to save on electricity bills, so she made any excuse to be in the open. Lauren needed people and social activities, and fresh air, and enjoyed learning and sightseeing.

On days when it did not make any sense to live the fast, hot and uncomfortable life with so many lifestyle restrictions, Lauren thought again of going back to her birthplace for good, due to the low cost of living and to enjoy the company of her relatives. That was her dream for later in life, but a couple of years before Frankie's death Lauren had developed lupus, a chronic debilitating condition, which required long-term treatment for her bones, skin and lung symptoms. Consequently, she chose to stay in the health system of the new home country where she had better entitlements to manage her underlying condition. Besides that, she had her group of friends, her predictable routine, and her younger sister Janna had recently come to live in the same city.

Lauren suffered from cataracts but feared surgery so never fixed the problem; as a result, she had two falls that both landed her in hospital. The medical advice after that was not to go out by herself, but she couldn't resist her desire to lead the independent life she was used to. Losing her vision was tolerable but losing independence after losing her sister was just more than she could bear. Around Christmas two years after Frankie's death, Lauren slipped again on the street and this time the damage was major and they kept her in rehabilitation for several weeks. She lost her appetite and became frail and confused. After the end of treatment she could not return to her apartment and instead, at the age of 67, was transferred to a nursing facility near her sister Janna but far away from me. It was all shocking as we were the same age and I was still working and healthy.

Lauren despised the nursing facility and refused to eat there. I wanted her discharged from the place to bring her to my home to live with me, but my family made me aware that she'd need 24-hour care and that I could not provide that for her. It broke my heart knowing that I had an extra room and time to help since I worked part-time, but couldn't help her keep a little freedom and have some normality. Janna had her own family problems and could not care for her full-time either. Perhaps now that she was retired for health reasons, she could have chosen to go back to her birth country and live in her own home? Nobody had said she couldn't but the subject did not come up.

After a few months our phone calls became very brief, and I suspected this was because she did not want people to know she was losing her mental capacity, mostly her memory. On the photos she shared by smart-phone, I noticed her hair had started to fall out and skin rashes were constant. I could sense she was deteriorating rapidly and did not need to be told that her end was near. I feared I would not be able to say my goodbyes in person, so my husband urged me to travel. I flew to be with her at the nursing home for a weekend. I was afraid of seeing her in such a deplorable state, but at the same time knew she needed a familiar face. After all, this moment was about her needs, not mine.

My visit was comforting for both of us because we hadn't seen each other in several months, but I was sad to see her frustration when she was not allowed to leave her room for a walk with me without assistance from the caretakers. She perceived this as an intrusion, antagonised the personnel because she was forgetful about who they were, and also made it clear she was not happy there. She confided in me, 'Sometimes all I want is to run the hell out of here.' I did not know how to help her but told her to be patient and that she would soon get transferred to a different facility.

During my stay, we went out for a nice dinner with her and Janna, and it surprised me that Lauren enjoyed our traditional food, trying all the different dishes. She looked so thin after starving herself at the facility. The next day we shared family pictures and stories of our college days, and I reassured her as to how many friends and family loved her.

When Lauren saw me visiting from far-away, I could tell she was beginning to realise that time was not on her side. There was no need to say it. That triggered her decision that she would be better off back in her homeland and decided to ask her sister Janna to arrange the trip. Unfortunately, by that time her health had declined too far and the specialists said her lung condition was too advanced and she could die during the flight home, so they could not give her a certificate of fitness to travel. It was too late to change her mind about where she wanted to die. She was torn by the hopelessness of her predicament. I was sad to leave her behind at the nursing home but I had to travel back to work.

A couple of weeks later she underwent extremely painful eye surgery to repair the tissue of one eye in preparation to implant the long-needed lens. There was hope Lauren could partly regain some independence to walk around safely. However, a few days following the surgery she had an infection and her kidneys started to fail; from there it cascaded into multiple complications. She was unable to eat by herself and so the staff decided to feed her through a tube in her stomach. I thought it was all senseless. From my conversations with Janna I knew the doctors were insisting on prolonging Lauren's life, which was against her wishes.

I found it ironic that the more the doctors did to save her life, the worse I felt watching them put her through such misery, knowing the result would be her inevitable death.

It had been many years since Lauren had wanted to die following her sister's death. I suggested it was best to let nature take its course, but her family consented to all treatments, perhaps because Lauren had never had a health directive prepared. She had only told me, her friend, about her real viewpoint and I had no decision-making power or her consent to reveal what she wanted. She had difficulty breathing, developed pneumonia, bleeding from her stomach and gut, and was given blood transfusions up until the day before she died, accompanied by her nephew and Janna. It was a double loss for Lauren, not being able to stop so much unwanted treatment and not being able to die at a place of her choice – such a disempowering experience.

She was cremated and the following month Janna took her ashes to our country. I'm certain that the quality of Lauren's end of life would have been a lot better had she gone back to her native country earlier, where she could have had family nearby and afforded the luxury of a community nurse who could have kept her symptoms under control and helped manage her medications. If Lauren had taken this route she could have died on her own terms, enjoying the time she had left in that familiar environment she longed for, without heroic medical interventions to stop her from closing the circle of life in the same place where she started.

What do you think?

- How do you feel about clinicians attempting everything they know to prolong the lives of people who have come to terms with their imminent mortality?
- Some people from different cultures are ambivalent about discussing death. When would be an appropriate time to discuss preferred place of death in your culture?

13

Knowing when to do nothing

Mr Ali, aged over 90 years, had been suffering from chronic kidney disease for many years and, added to that, had underlying heart problems and lung cancer that had spread to other organs. He was no longer receiving cancer therapy because there was nothing else to offer, yet he was still taking tablets to lower his cholesterol, which caused him more harm than good as these drugs gave him muscle pain, and he wasn't going to live long enough to benefit from their preventive effects. Worse, he was still attending dialysis sessions which gave him fatigue, nausea, itchy skin and disturbed his sleep most nights. He could not even eat whatever he wanted as dialysis goes hand in hand with a restricted diet. All of these side-effects of dialysis robbed him of decent quality of life in his last year of life.

Except he didn't know it was his last phase. His family knew his prognosis was poor and they were well aware that he was dying, but chose not to tell him and let him continue dialysis regardless of the lack of physical benefit. They believed the emotional benefit of thinking his disease was under control was a good enough justification for continuing a futile treatment. It was just not part of their culture to take hope away or give up on precious life.

Medical technology has come a long way since the first dialysis machine was invented in 1943. These days there are so many possibilities for transplants, diagnostic imaging, vaccines that are updated yearly, surgery for unborn babies, chemotherapy, antibiotics, immunological agents, even improved understanding of our genetic makeup for personalised treatments which they call 'precision medicine'. But how much progress have clinicians made, once they know there is no cure, on disclosing honest prognosis to patients and families? I am not talking about telling patients exact date of death because there is always uncertainty in medicine. I am wondering whether the new generations of medical and nursing graduates have really become more advanced communicators of bad news than their predecessors? Have they learnt to identify earlier the people who are dying so they can compassionately tell them approximately how long they have to live, what to expect and empathetically mention how to get ready?

I had chosen to work in dialysis units after graduating as a mature-aged registered nurse. The role was so interesting, and the technology was out of this world to me all those years back. I marvelled at how this machine could play the part of a human kidney by removing waste products from the blood, balancing fluids and electrolytes all at the same time, and prolong a person's life. Yes, prolonging lives was seen as equivalent to saving lives – what health professionals are meant to be doing, right? I wasn't wise enough then to think there might be an alternative view.

I cared for different types of patients and found that there were more elderly than young. Dialysis sessions consisted of four to five hours on the machine three times a week, where large cannulas were placed in patients' arm blood vessels, or catheters were inserted into their hearts or jugular veins, to access their blood and link it to the extracorporeal circuit to clean impurities. This process basically prolonged life, and for some patients this was appropriate, especially for the young, for whom the option of a kidney transplant could be explored so they could go on with a relatively normal life. For very old people with a terminal illness, transplant and going back to normal life were not an option, but I do not recall us – the treating team – discussing the quality of that life we were prolonging.

We assumed we had succeeded if the patient completed a session with good laboratory test results and without catching an infection or getting another complication.

For the first few months I was completely focused on learning the dialysis technology, getting to know the patients' long and complex medical histories and brushing up on the administrative duties of team work. I did get really good at my job and was a whizz with the technology and the patients became like family to me, given how often I saw them and had chats during the long hours on the dialysis machine.

Some patients looked resentful about their predicament, while others were resigned to the boring hours they had to spend at the hospital instead of enjoying these with their families. Others just did some reading or watched TV and took the sessions with a grain of salt. But there was more to my job than the technical aspects – situations I had not necessarily been trained for, like being aware that patients had not been fully informed of the lifestyle implications of agreeing to dialysis. Some had no idea of their real chances of survival, or that they were not eligible for a kidney transplant because it was too late for them to benefit.

The ethical dilemmas of when dialysis should be terminated for some patients preyed on my mind sometimes. You see, some patients were very elderly (over 80 years) and had many problems – not just their kidneys had failed. It was not uncommon to see patients like Mr Ali, who also had heart conditions, and lung problems, cancers, diabetes and the silent enemy, frailty. I would look at the patients who were very old and quite unwell being wheeled in for yet another dialysis session, faces gaunt, ashen-looking skin and a sense of palpable sadness or a tiredness that has no words to describe it but clearly demonstrated how they really felt about the whole process. Their well-meaning families persisted in ensuring they attended the session as if there was no alternative. Did they know there was a choice? I wonder.

To prevent infections, families could not stay with patients to distract them or make their day stay more bearable. Children could not visit. Pets were not allowed. I always had an affinity towards the patients who were seriously ill and slowly dying. I gave wholeheartedly of my time, touch, empathy and wisdom of the continuum of birth, life and death as I saw it, all the while respecting and using sensitivity towards all cultures, beliefs and religions.

I reflected one day on the patients I was being allocated during my shifts and noticed that I was always given those who were not long for this world. When I asked my colleagues why this was the case, they responded by saying, 'Oh, you do such a good job with the dying. Whatever it is that you do to sooth the dying, it helps and some patients ask for you specifically.' I thought to myself that's a nice compliment. Then I thought, 'Oh, no! Have my friends been watching me ministering to the dying and talking to the patients that could no longer talk?' I mean, I would have some really long chats with those who could speak and those who could not regardless, because I believed they could hear me.

It was comforting to know that the other nurses felt similarly to myself on the topic of sensing when to cease dialysis because it would be most humane and allow patients to die with dignity surrounded by those they loved, not in the hospital with machines beeping or with staff performing resuscitation in an attempt to prolong a life that had reached fullness and desired peace. Yet some discussions and decisions to suspend dialysis were delayed unnecessarily due to the specialists' busy schedules and to clinical inertia. Our role and their job focused mostly on delivering the service, keeping the health system functioning and only occasionally on taking that step back to see if patients really wanted or gained from the blood purification ritual in the long term.

We nurses would discuss freely during our breaks at morning tea or handovers how the topic of death was so sensitive that we found it difficult, even as healthcare professionals, to start conversations with patients and their families around what plans needed to be made. Our undergraduate training on breaking bad news or spelling out the dying process for patients had been minimal. I believe the entire experience involved a few hours over a couple of weeks.

There was also the other side of the coin. Sometimes patients' families would tell us nurses privately that the doctor had advised that their loved one should stop treatment because there was no more that could be done but the family disagreed. Conflict with health professionals' recommendation near the end of life is commonplace when patients or families have not been kept informed of the disease progression along the way, so they may feel abandoned and neglected rather than understand this is the most humane way to stop the suffering of their loved one. This is something that could also be prevented if there was no taboo around the 'D-word' (as in 'D' for 'Death').

Mr Ali spoke little English but we were able to communicate and I looked after him on many occasions. He would say, 'Nurse, I think I'm dying,' and I would say, 'And how do you feel about that?' Then he would reply, 'I'm afraid.' I would hold his hand and he would look at me with the saddest eyes, like a child and say, 'Don't leave me; just hold my hand and talk to me.'

I asked Mr Ali if he was religious and he said he was and that he believed in Allah and prayed a lot. When I asked him why he was so afraid of dying, he said, 'Because I am not confident I did well enough in this life and am unsure if I would be going to heaven or not.' He also wanted to know what I thought about this matter and if I thought he would be alright. I did give him a reassuring answer, that yes I did believe that there was a God or higher consciousness that was the same as his Allah and that we were all here on earth to experience life and we made choices, good and bad, and that he should not be afraid to go to the other side when he was ready. We could silently pray together, I suggested, for safe passage: me in my way and he in his, with good effect. We did not need any more words in either his language or mine. The connection was made. Because grief and end-of-life transcend languages and cultural barriers.

I did ask Mr Ali if he had spoken to his family about his feelings and he said he had not because they probably had chosen to think he did not know; they did not understand that he felt dead already and that he was fully aware of what was going on; he said they are all just worrying about him dying and trying to keep him alive at any cost. I asked him if he wanted to continue dialysis and he said no, but when he said that to his family, they told him he must keep coming so he obliged. It was not in his culture to give up.

He continued to attend dialysis sessions and the last time I saw him he was so distressed, gasping and panicked because he could not breathe properly due to his lung cancer. He hardly spoke that day except to call out for a nurse to hold his hand and reassure him. Thankfully I was his assigned nurse that day. I prayed for him, held his hand and wiped the sweat off his brow and said goodbye because I knew I would not see him again. I suppose he knew that too. He passed away overnight after I had finished my shift. I am not sure if his family was with him.

I wished families could talk to loved ones about their impending death and the plans that need to be made for the dying and for the surviving relatives. I understand, too, how difficult it is to talk about death for some people. It can be challenging even for trained health workers who deal with dying people on a regular basis. However, this can be improved with communications training and, if done well, dying from old age and advanced chronic illness can be a smooth transition that also helps ease the bereavement period for families. I have heard people say expressions like 'She had a beautiful death' or 'He died the way he lived: in control of his own destiny', so I know it is possible. I do believe that if we, as human beings, change the way we view death and understand that it is as natural as being born, it is part of the life cycle, a great difference can be made. Clinicians, patients and families could decide earlier to stop treatments that are burdensome, futile and unwanted by patients and instead we could transition them to the supportive and palliative pathway of care they really need and deserve.

What do you think?

- How do you feel about the option of 'doing nothing' or 'letting go' when patients have had enough and there is no real prospect of survival with a good quality of life?
- If the avoidance of conversations about death across culture hinders the right of very sick people to die well, what could be done to start normalising these discussions?
- Whose role is it to bring the topic up – the patient or the family? And why?

14

Not for resuscitation

Nicki was admitted to the ward for dehydration and malnutrition. Or so her family thought. There was no urgency from the relatives, as if this was just another symptom of the long-standing illness that had ravaged her body; a pebble on the road. The reality was, cancer had relentlessly spread through her body over several months, consuming her previously filled figure and unforgivingly ageing her face. Staff were talking about how she was 'Not doing well' and 'Deteriorating.' She had obviously been to many specialist appointments over the past year but the word '*Dying*' had not been discussed with her or her husband; neither had an advance resuscitation plan or advance care directive been put in place.

It was late at night and, if Nicki's heart had stopped there and then, the nurses would have had to start CPR until a specialist could come and initiate the conversation with the family towards a decision to stop or continue.

Predictably for us clinicians – although not for the family – within hours she deteriorated further and, because her vital signs had reached the 'red zone', this meant that she met criteria for calling the rapid response team to come and 'rescue' her. I was part of that team but not the lead that night. Nobody treating Nicki took the initiative of discussing the option of comfort care.

Consequently, I stepped up and told Nicki in my softest, gentlest voice, 'You need all your family in now. We're going to make you as comfortable as possible.'

We asked her husband to come to the room and he turned up with a very alarmed look. While he was clenching Nicki's hand I started: 'I don't want to give you false hope. Your wife is dying. We can only keep her comfortable. Call the children in as she doesn't have long – hours at best.'

He broke down and sobbed uncontrollably but his wife was accepting of her situation. She was in and out of consciousness after that. The look on their faces struck me as it indicated it was all unexpected to them despite witnessing her long illness with such a progressive decline. This can happen if clinicians don't warn families early of the anticipated disease trajectory. Healthcare professionals need to practise difficult conversations, but when terms for death and dying are explained as '*not responding to treatment*' or '*not doing well*', then we miss opportunities for clear messaging to patients and loved ones. These are the people for whom the death was 'unexpected'. The husband murmured, 'No-one has said anything about dying before' to which I replied: 'I'm so sorry you have not had a hint of how serious her illness was. I use this blunt language now because she's going through the active phase of dying. I don't want you to waste precious minutes. Say what you need to her before she goes.'

I dream of the day when we can normalise these conversations in a planned way, before a crisis, not in the last days of someone's life. Just as we have asked families to let loved ones know their wishes for organ donation when they are not near death, we must now ask families to have the discussions around advanced care directives and resuscitation care plans long before they are unable to speak for themselves. However, it is a reality that death and dying are subjects that many don't feel comfortable discussing.

Such discussion brings about thoughts and feelings of our own vulnerability. It causes awkward silences.

Unfortunately, the unspoken code across health services of not using the words '*death*' and '*dying*' has been practised for years. The language has been replaced with '*goals of care*' to soften the harsh message that it is all final, impossible to fix. This delay in truth-telling results in patients being actively and sometimes aggressively treated until the last day of life, when they could have been using their last weeks with family, spared futile medicalisation. This disguised communication keeps the patient and family on hold, waiting for the words to be said. They cling to hope until someone mercifully confirms death is actually happening.

That's where *'Not for Resuscitation'* (NFR) orders come in. These carry a lot of uncertainty. There is much confusion around these orders, both within the healthcare environment and in the community. Many people think they will not be cared for if they have a *'Do Not Resuscitate'* order in place. This is not true. 'What if my condition improves?' is one frequent question, and 'How long do they last?' The answers are:

- 'If the condition is reversible, we will *not* propose or issue a "*Not for Resuscitation*" order.

- 'If the situation is irreversible, we will *not* abandon any patient.'

I want families to understand that if their loved one has a *'Not for Resuscitation'* order, s/he will be looked after and their pain, breathlessness and other symptoms will be treated. The only thing we will not do is attempt CPR if their heart stops.

Hospital staff know that NFRs issued in hospital can also be challenged by the patient and/or families later, so the orders can be renewed or reconsidered on a future admission.

I also often hear the question: 'Is the NFR valid if it is made outside of the healthcare environment?' This is asked not only by families but also by health professionals. In principle, if the person has an advance care directive produced at home, or with a lawyer, stating they object to CPR in the current state of health, then clinicians need to accept the order as valid and align treatment with the patient's wishes. This is true of where I practise but, of course, may change from one healthcare system to another.

If a patient falls into irreversible deterioration while in hospital, we have to ask families: 'If your loved one's heart stops, would you want us to resuscitate him/her?' Choosing whether or not resuscitation is to be performed for their loved one can cause immense decisional conflict and long-lasting guilt if no prior discussion has been held with the patient. I too have struggled with patients' decisions when it is not clear which way is best. However, once the conversation turns to open and honest communication, patients express their values, and resuscitation plans can be explained in terms that the patient and family understand. It is then that decisions can be well informed and a sense of 'doing the right thing' for the patient emerges.

I faced one of those dilemmas with Garth, a patient in his 50s who'd had enough of living. He had spent the previous four years in and out of hospital. He'd always given us the impression that one day he would not survive ICU or be able to go home, but so far he always had and not surviving ICU remained a thing in the future.

As a nurse I'm not used to letting go if there is something else to be done for a relatively young person, yet Garth requested the conversation about not surviving as he wanted to formalise an NFR in his medical record and cease active treatments. I was able to openly discuss death and dying at this stage as I knew death was not imminent, but I couldn't separate the fact that Garth could still go home and watch TV after a few days of ICU if he allowed us to continue. However, he didn't want that anymore.

The family didn't agree with Garth's decision either, but once he had made his wishes known and the family had had to eventually come to terms with it, it was time for Garth to say goodbye.

I struggled with the concept of him having an NFR order and wanting to enact it so soon, even though I had helped him come to the decision. I had to remind myself, 'This is not about you; it's about him.' For that reason, the most painful part was when Garth requested that I attend when life support was withdrawn. A privilege of healthcare professionals is that we are there when a baby takes its first breath and when someone takes their last, but in Garth's case I was not able to fulfil his wishes to be there. I know he was at peace with his decision, but I still had doubts: 'What if he could recover from this setback? What if further treatment becomes available...? What if...?!'

I knew the right decision was being made, aligned with his personal values and I fully supported his decision – in principle – but I did not want to see him die. I didn't need him to be watching me be upset. He had enough staff and family around him. Meanwhile, I could be present to witness and accompany another older and sicker patient for whom there was no real prospect of recovery.

Yes, I have known people who are very ready to take on the subject of death. I vividly remember Greta, a 70-year-old patient with advanced lung cancer, former nurse and former smoker, who had given up smoking 10 years before diagnosis. In my recollection I am sitting in on a conversation a hospital doctor is having with her.

'Tell me how I'm going to die. I need to know,' she asks the specialist in a very brave and no-nonsense way. He is evidently uncomfortable with this direct question, fixing himself on the chair, and I am waiting for him to describe the process. It is frustrating that I cannot intervene as I'm 'only the nurse'. No matter that I have 28 years' experience as a member of the rapid response team. I have been watching people inevitably die, helping them die comfortably, and stopping people from dying by resuscitating them, all as part of my job. I can talk about death without all the euphemisms. I can see the doctor stumbling for a couple of minutes before he can find the words to explain the worst case scenario to her.

As Greta has already had courses of radiotherapy and chemotherapy, by the time she is told she has brain metastases, she says, 'That's enough', even though additional treatments have been offered to give her more time. More time won't do as she knows she'll lose the ability to make decisions in the not-too-distant future and that to her is an unacceptable way of living. She is clearly aware the end is in sight, and she is ready to face it. So she tells me, as her closest nurse who has known her for years: 'I need you to be my advocate; speak on my behalf to make the hard decisions on treatment from now on.'

Yes, I've been a patient surrogate decision-maker many times, and in the case of Greta, I knew that a 'Not for resuscitation' order was in her best interest. Many people don't understand that resuscitation is an aggressive and heroic form of treatment and usually not as successful as portrayed in the movies. It can have serious health complications even if the person survives CPR. I will not describe them here but believe me, there are states of health that could be worse than death, when the quality of remaining life is poorer than before admission to hospital; and the family suffers too. Families who still put pressure on clinicians to administer futile CPR on relatives with advanced irreversible illness should reconsider whether they are doing it for themselves because they cannot accept the inevitable or are making this request on behalf of their loved one because they still believe there is benefit.

It is not uncommon to see 'unexpected' deaths also happen in the case of patients with dementia, as families often don't recognise this condition as a progressive, incurable, life-limiting illness, perhaps because it has a subtle and gradual onset, and is drawn out over many years. If the possibility of meaningful survival after CPR is gone, a cardiac arrest does not warrant a resuscitation attempt. To those requests, I have in the past replied along the lines of 'Medically, there is no benefit. We need to put your mum first. She's suffering. She has forgotten how to eat, swallow, walk, who you are, who she is, and we all have our time to go. This is her time. We may not know when exactly, but CPR will not be attempted, and no emergency rescue calls will be triggered. It would not be in her best interest to carry out resuscitation.' Those unambiguous terms usually help families to understand and agree to an NFR order. I still feel for them as I know how hard it is to lose your mum, but someone has to make the difficult decisions.

I don't think I should make an apology for being so direct. I can't know the family politics or whether they are putting their needs above those of the patient. This is my job: to be the patient's advocate in their last hours. However, when resuscitation could be more harmful than beneficial it should not be considered. The preference for a NFR order is a discussion that we all should be having jointly with families as we age or as early as incurable illnesses are diagnosed, or when our health starts to decline to the point that makes us visit hospitals more frequently.

It doesn't matter whether you're old or young: we need to take the taboo out of discussions around death and dying. 'What music would you like to hear in your last moments? Who would you like to be present when you are on your death bed?' These things are as important as what drugs you take for your illnesses and at what time. We do not want to leave our families with the burden of guessing and choosing for us. We need to be involved in our own end-of-life decision-making and personalise it, just as we take time to plan weddings, pregnancies, house purchases and farewell parties. Take the time to write down what you would be prepared to live with, and what you would consider unacceptable for your send off. Set treatment goals with your treating team. Help them to help you.

What do you think?

- Think of at least two ways in which a '*Not for resuscitation*' order can be a positive step.
- Just as with NFR orders, when do you think a '*Not for hospital transfer*' order would be beneficial or appropriate?

15

A celebration of life on his own terms

Some people love life but live as if they were ready to die. Samuel was one of those. An ex-military man who had held a highly valuable and responsible job in the service, he had been awarded many medals throughout his career.

Samuel knew he had only a short amount of time left with his family when he was diagnosed with an aggressive form of cancer which had not responded to treatment. I had known him for three years as his community nurse, in which role I would attend his home regularly to perform health checks and I had become very close to Samuel and his family over those years.

Samuel would often speak with me in detail and reflect on his days in the service, which I felt was a real privilege as many ex-servicemen don't. He was a modest man and would always credit his mates with his achievements at work. However, his biggest achievement by far – and he was not modest about this – was his family. He adored his family just as they adored him. He was proud of his children and grandchildren and how well they had done throughout the years.

Over the three years that I had known Samuel, he and I had spoken on a couple occasions about what he would want when the end of his life was near. He was open about this topic and wanted to discuss it with me. In fact, he was the one to initiate the conversation, which was a relief to me as I had limited experience in these sensitive discussions. University courses have limited practical training on breaking bad news to patients before we are released to practise as clinicians in the real world. He would often remind me that he had lived a great life and was very proud of his family and that death did not scare him as he grew older. He alluded to the fact that he had seen so many of his mates lose their lives young during war that he felt blessed to have been able to get this far as an 'old man' with so many things in his life to be proud of.

Samuel would often say he was concerned that his family and friends would be greatly saddened by his death. He did not want this for them. When the time came, he would want the end of his life to be a celebration.

He held strong views on where he wanted to spend his final days when he would no longer be able to look after himself and he had shared these views with me, his local doctor of more than 20 years, and with his children. He was adamant that he did not want to spend his remaining life in his home if he was to lose independence. These strong views largely came from his own lived experience of caring for his wife at home; she had died five years before having had Alzheimer's disease and he had not only been her loving husband but had also acted as her sole caregiver for many years. Samuel and his wife would not have done it any other way, he would assure me. He often remarked how he had still very much enjoyed the remaining years with his wife although her mental and physical condition was deteriorating rapidly. He felt privileged to have been her caregiver, but he also knew the unconditional commitment and personal sacrifice this entailed and he did not want that situation for his children. He did not want them acting as his caregivers: 'They have their own families, their own responsibilities, their own lives to live'.

Samuel would say that he would prefer to be in a hostel or someplace where he would have access to ongoing nursing support; where his family could visit whenever they wished, but did not have to carry the responsibility for attending to his personal needs and caring for him day in, day out. He dreaded the drastic change of his relationship with them from fun-loving to dutiful. He did not want them showering him, toileting him and – as Samuel saw this – 'giving up their lives'. He certainly did not want to burden them. He wanted them to remember him as the warm father and grandpa he had been, not as the debilitated patient he had become.

Despite Samuel's strong preference not to spend his final days at home with his family acting as his carers, his children felt very differently. They wanted their dad at home. They loved him. They did not want him going to a facility where his carers would be people who didn't know him, and he did not know them. There was much apprehension about the treatment Samuel would receive from well-meaning strangers. His family truly felt that they could provide the best care, love and support he would need. They knew their dad best. Their childhoods had been full of bedtime stories of military adventures, family meals by the fire and holidays in the bush. They wanted to thank him for creating those memories by being around to cater for his every need.

The son argued, 'Dad, we're in a pretty good financial position to support you at home and could take time off work if needed.' The daughter reassured him she would also have the time to share responsibilities to manage his day-to-day personal needs. They saw this as a natural justice, where their father had cared for them for so many years, they wanted to be able to now be the ones to look after him during his illness.

Samuel, however, could not be persuaded by his family. He had thought about how he wanted to live the last part of his life and that did not involve being cared for by his children. He understood that his family were doing this out of love for him and that they wanted him close, but he told them he knew the responsibility of being a carer for a loved one and, although very rewarding, it could also be extremely difficult. He would never want that for his children whom he loved so dearly.

The family found it incredibly hard to accept the fact that their father did not want to spend the end of his life at home. Most older people want to die at home surrounded by loved ones and many unfortunately die in an institution surrounded by equipment and medical staff. Samuel had the opportunity to remain at home but was choosing not to take it. They could not understand why their dad would not want them to care for him.

This caused much tension for both the children and Samuel as neither wanted to disappoint the other, yet both thought they were doing the right thing. Many families do not realise how complicated, time-consuming, expensive, physically onerous and emotionally draining the role of informal caregiver is. Despite their love and available time to help, they might not be able to manage all of their father's symptoms or nursing tasks and this job could lead to depression and burnout.[4] Samuel knew this from first-hand experience but had never communicated it to them during their mother's illness.

This was becoming very distressing for both Samuel and his children as they had such very different views about what should happen when Samuel came to need full-time care. Samuel felt that it would be best if everyone held a discussion about what the future might hold.

Dying is distressing for all involved and can be especially distressing for those who are caring for the dying patient. However, caring for a dying patient can also be one of the most rewarding roles undertaken by a nurse, carer or medical professional. Having the privilege to be able to care for and support a person as they make their way out of this world to wherever is next is something only very few of us get to experience. The children wanted that privilege.

They felt it was the least they could do. They were prepared for the lifestyle change. They knew their father's strong character and needed someone outside of the family to help resolve this impasse.

I was invited to join in the discussion during a health-check visit I paid at Samuel's house. The family were all present and I was asked to discuss the reality of caring for a loved one at home. We talked about outside services, equipment, home modification, out-of-pocket expenses and multiple visits to healthcare providers, all of which the children were very willing to be involved in and wanted to go ahead with when the time came. I mentioned the satisfaction of giving back to their dad, the learning of new nursing skills, and the building of memories that would help the informal caregivers cope with grieving after Samuel's passing. I also mentioned the stress, intermittent frustration, sleepless nights, backache, deprivation of leisure time and other potential negative experiences that could come with the responsibility of caring for a loved one towards the end of their life.

However, despite the support that could be available, ultimately this was Samuel's decision and he had made up his mind that he did not want to be in his home. It is a very personal thing how some patients are comfortable and others feel undignified with relatives taking care of all their bodily needs.

After a lengthy discussion, with much debate, laughter and tears, a decision was finally reached among all involved that Samuel's wishes were to be respected and upheld. It was understood that, although he had decided that he wanted to be cared for in supported accommodation (the hostel/aged-care facility had not been chosen at this stage), the family would still remain the biggest and most important part of his life.

A couple months after our family meeting, Samuel's son phoned to inform me that his dad had moved into his chosen supported accommodation. He said Samuel was still in very high spirits despite his health deteriorating; however, his pain was under control and the family visited often. I wished the family all the best and asked him to give Samuel a big 'hello' from me. Samuel's son also expressed to me during this phone call that the family was satisfied now with Samuel's decision as to where he wanted to spend the last months of his life. They felt great relief that they were all given the opportunity to discuss each family members' concern and wishes. Even though he would have still liked having his dad at home, they could do nothing more than watch these events naturally unfold and provide Samuel with the love and support that he had shown them and that he himself deserved.

What do you think?

- In some cultures, dying from long-term illness at home is the preferred way and in others it is something to be avoided. How do you feel about it?
- Some informal caregivers find it burdensome on some level and a privilege at the same time to walk the journey together with someone who is dying. Do you think guilt is a driving factor for the decision about where to care for a loved one? Does it outweigh practicality?

16

The advocate and translator

Dad had been fit and healthy his entire life and was still going strong: walking several miles every day, practising yoga and tai-chi, no apparent health concerns and no medications. He became ill one weekend after one of his regular walks, during which he said he had got very cold and caught a chill, which seemed then to develop into a chest infection with breathing trouble despite antibiotics.

He went by ambulance to an emergency assessment unit (EAU) at a large teaching hospital in the city and I was able to go to the hospital with him. It was early evening, the EAU unit was crowded, noisy and very busy, but there was clearly order in among the frantic busyness. Dad was promptly and efficiently assessed by the nursing staff, a registrar and, later, the EAU consultant. A late-night bedside ultrasound revealed that he had severe pulmonary leakage, with a couple of litres of fluid pressing on his lungs.

The next day after an X-ray and further tests, the fluid was drained, and Dad felt significantly better so he was transferred to a ward. After a few days he was eating well, sitting up in bed to read the news and sending emails on his iPad, and could be weaned off the oxygen he had been having since admission. The medical staff and students commented on how supple he was, able to so easily touch his toes when leaning forward as they listened to his chest; he seemed quite chuffed with that. He was also pleased when the consultant told him that he was the last to be seen on the ward rounds because he seemed to be the healthiest person on the ward.

Mum and I were full of hope but the only one, ongoing niggle for both the medical team and for us was that all of the tests were inconclusive; after a week in hospital the consultants were unable to provide a definitive diagnosis for what had caused the fluid in his chest. When we asked directly about the possibility of cancer, the medical team were open about discussing their thinking and rationale; none of the diagnostic tests to-date had indicated malignancy so they still suspected atypical pneumonia, but they wanted to be sure. He was finally discharged with a referral to the respiratory team as an outpatient for a biopsy to clarify the remaining suspicious shadows on his lungs.

Dad ended up being readmitted to hospital before his scheduled biopsy as the fluid returned in less than a week and another two litres were drained away. The biopsy had to be cancelled as his blood pressure dropped, and he was exhausted and increasingly frail. A week later his heart went into atrial fibrillation. We then knew it was serious as the consultant from his ward called us to come back to the hospital to see her as soon as possible.

Dad had been stabilised a little but he looked dreadful – pale, clammy and clearly anxious. The consultant explained that the new X-rays had revealed a progression of the shadows on Dad's lungs and they thought it could be either tuberculosis (TB – very unlikely but still possible) or a rapidly progressing lymphoma. An ICU specialist would come to assess Dad so the consultant asked Mum if she had ever discussed with Dad his wishes with respect to intensive versus end-of-life care, and interventions such as going on a ventilator.

This was the first time I think that Mum and I really faced the reality that this might not be a temporary illness for Dad. It felt quite surreal, as though I had almost known all along this was what was coming, and yet also a complete shock to hear it stated so clearly by the doctor that Dad might not actually recover.

In 60 years of marriage, my parents had never discussed what they would do in the situation of one of them having a terminal illness, and potentially needing resuscitation or intubation for a ventilator. The consultant asked if we wished to speak with Dad about it now, or if we preferred for her to do it. My mother opted for the latter so the consultant went to speak with Dad to explain the situation and ask about his wishes.

I'm not sure how long the doctor was away, maybe 20 minutes. My mother was visibly distressed and only really beginning to absorb the seriousness of Dad's condition. We sat holding hands and talking about what we thought Dad would want and could not imagine that he would want to go on life support if there was no purpose to it other than to prolong his life in a potentially unconscious and terminal state.

When the consultant returned she told us that Dad had been quite clear that he did not wish to be placed on a ventilator unless there was a real chance of recovery. I was not sure what that actually meant, particularly as we still did not know the final biopsy results, yet I had understood that Dad might well be facing a terminal illness. The consultant had been gentle but she clearly felt the need to have this conversation with Dad sooner rather than later.

We returned to Dad's bedside to wait for the ICU consultant. Dad was still very pale and breathless, but able talk and drink some tea. I asked him if the doctor had explained what was happening (yes) and if he had any questions that he wanted to ask us (no). We didn't discuss it any further at that time, neither what the doctor had explained to him nor the details of Dad's wishes. I think neither of my parents could face having that conversation in front of everyone else on the ward, and Mum was afraid of crying in front of Dad and upsetting him. All along I think they both just wanted to remain positive for each other for as long as possible. The ward nursing staff were clearly aware of what had been happening; they made us all cups of tea and pulled the curtain around the bed for some privacy as there were three other patients in Dad's part of the ward and some had visitors, though really we hardly noticed them.

The intensive care consultant arrived soon after; he conducted a brief clinical examination, and offered to meet with us to explain what was happening once Dad had been connected to the various machines, tubes and other gadgets, and had settled in the life-sustaining phase of treatment.

I have very clear memories of the meeting we had with our intensive care consultant. He was a very eloquent communicator and exuded both competence and compassion. He told us that while Dad was relatively stable there was a real risk he might deteriorate overnight. I felt almost numb with stress and tiredness but so grateful for the empathic and gentle manner with which he spoke to us. He gave us as much time as we needed, answered all of our questions (mostly mine as I seemed to have become Dad's advocate and Mum's translator), and provided detailed explanations.

While my parents were born abroad, they had lived in the UK for nearly 50 years, were fluent in English, and Mum had worked as a lab technician at the hospital for many decades. Yet over the two months that Dad had been sick, they had often spoken about the challenges of communicating with the medical teams and other hospital staff. When Dad was on the wards they often wanted to know more about what the doctors were thinking, but rarely asked their questions directly of the staff. Instead, they would prefer to ask me questions about what had been said after the doctors or nurses had left. For Mum in particular, not knowing what was happening was always far more anxiety provoking than getting an update, even when the news was hard to bear. Yet she felt uncomfortable directing her questions to the doctors.

During the time it took for the biopsy results to come back, Dad had become visibly weaker and found it harder and harder to breathe. At least in ICU he had 24-hour one-on-one nursing care. He also had his own room because they hadn't yet totally excluded the small risk of TB, so for a period of some days, everyone who entered his room had to wear masks. These made it more difficult to communicate and Dad couldn't hear properly what people were saying around him unless they lifted their mask and spoke directly to him. However, the relief of being able to stop using them so that we could talk properly again was totally negated by the knowledge that by excluding TB we were left with the ominous diagnosis of lymphoma. That would not be better news.

The results finally arrived with the terrible news confirming the aggressive, untreatable cancer, which meant Dad was basically now receiving palliative care. He was not responding to the ICU treatment and now it was only a matter of time. The doctor didn't specify how long, but said he would allow Dad to stay in ICU for as long as they had room. Most of all we were grateful for his reassurance that they wouldn't let Dad suffer when his lungs eventually failed, and that he wouldn't choke to death.

What everyone noticed who dealt with Dad was how incredibly alert and yet calm and peaceful he seemed during his time in hospital. He was a very religious man and was deeply comforted by visits from his local parish priest who came to pray with him and perform the last rites. The priest told us that in all his years of visiting people in hospital he had never seen anyone so peaceful and accepting of their oncoming death. And although Dad started to receive morphine for his laboured breathing, he somehow retained a clear head and was able to dictate emails to say goodbye to his friends and colleagues, and hear us read their replies. He only lived for a few more days.

The night before Dad died, I stayed at the hospital catching a few hours of restless sleep in the little room set aside for family who needed to stay over. I had sent Mum home earlier that evening to try to sleep as we had been at the hospital all day again and I was concerned by how unwell and tired she looked. I was back with Dad by around 5.00 am and Mum arrived a couple of hours later. It was clear Dad had waited for her to return but wasn't going to survive the day. In the last few hours of his life, as he found it harder and harder to breathe, there was a choice between increasing the morphine or stopping the medication that was maintaining his heart and blood pressure. Dad was conscious enough to be able to make the choice to withdraw the latter. Mum and I were both with him when he died at 9.20 that morning, each holding one hand as he took his last few breaths and slipped away. We were able to say what we needed to say in those remaining few hours, and the last thing I told him before he died was how proud I was of him. It was the first time I had told my father I was proud of who he was. I was in my 50s and he was in his 80s and it had never even occurred to me to say it before, but in that moment I realised how important it was for me to say, and for him to hear. Dad held my hand, and with the priest's rosary still around his wrist, allowed himself to leave.

Mum and I continued to sit quietly in the room for a while after Dad had died, but I don't really remember for how long or what we said. Eventually, one of the nurses who had cared for him overnight came to say goodbye after her shift and the nurse who had started the new shift explained we would be contacted by the hospital bereavement service and gave us a pamphlet outlining the next steps. As we packed up our things and left, the nurse gave us Dad's wedding ring and the rosary he had been holding. She told us she was going to clean Dad's body and prepare it to go to the morgue.

In reflecting on this time, I have come to appreciate how important it is for people who are sick and frightened to have someone among their family or friends who is able to be an advocate for them. I have realised that, apart from being present as a daughter, my role throughout Dad's illness and death was also to be my parents' translator and advocate. For both of my parents, communication was particularly challenging because of their very poor hearing, combined with the fact that English is their second language. Any regional or foreign accents were especially difficult for them to understand. As a result, they were very dependent on all of the hospital staff being willing to speak far more slowly and loudly than they might normally have done, but they felt reluctant to keep asking people to repeat things when they didn't slow down or speak up. It was particularly noticeable that whenever a senior doctor took time to slowly and carefully explain to my parents what was happening and why, it felt genuinely empowering for them and was greatly appreciated. We all felt more valued and cared for as a result of those communications, which enabled us to deal with reality rather than to get lost in speculations.

For me to have been able to be with my parents throughout the ordeal – to help Mum and Dad navigate the hospital systems, ask their questions on their behalf, and explain to them the things they didn't understand – was a gift that made a world of difference for all of us.

In memory of my father

When father died, he was 83 but it was not something we expected. Although the gender statistics are pretty much against women dying earlier than men, Mum had always insisted she wanted to go first. Yet, despite the pain and sadness of losing him, we have at least been consoled by knowing that – if there is such a thing – my father had a '*good death*'. In his last few days he felt privileged to have the best quality care and the opportunity to make treatment decisions and tie the loose ends with his friends. This reflection is to honour his memory, and to thank those who cared for him and enabled that to be the case.

What do you think?

- If you have you been an advocate or translator for someone who could not communicate in a health service, how did you feel representing their wishes?
- In your view, what circumstances would make a death 'good'?
- Do you feel it is okay for relatives to take the role of translators or should professional translators be employed for the task? What would be advantages and disadvantages of each?

17

The right not to know

I have spent most of my life doing things the hard way. I had a troubled childhood, plagued with memories of a dysfunctional family, and I left home for good to save myself from domestic hell and pursue success elsewhere. Or so I thought. Instead, my adolescence was filled with illicit activity, drug experimentation, alcohol abuse and less than desirable companions. Eventually I went back to finish high school when I was in my 20s and graduated, but my alcohol dependence persisted and made me unfit for many potential jobs. My drinking problem eventually led to a serious car accident that left me hemiplegic when I was in my 30s and my then girlfriend abandoned me so I never married or had children. Consequently, I've lived at my mum's place on and off for the past three decades. I refused to acknowledge my disability, went back to work in a different occupation and acted as if nothing was the matter, rarely mentioning my condition over the years. '*Denial*' has been my best ally.

When I was diagnosed with stage-3 kidney cancer in my 50s and had major surgery to remove it, I also brushed off the episode despite almost dying during the hospitalisation due to massive bleeding and other complications that confined me to intensive care for a couple of months. After I was discharged, I knew my drinking had to stop as I came to terms with having one less kidney and diminished capacity to clear alcohol. According to the statistics of that time, I had a 45% chance of surviving for three years, but once I had decided I had '*recovered*,' my loved ones endured again the social and emotional burden associated with my repeat drunkenness and the trauma of my self-alienation from family and friends for the following three years. They all practically gave up trying to help me detox. Until stage 4 hit me in my early 60s, that is.

When I received that 'terminal' diagnosis, my mother quietly and deliberately stopped eating and took minimal fluids in the hope that death would come to take her. She did not, however, discontinue the medicines that kept her illnesses at bay. I think she must have been ambivalent about whether to be there to support me till the end or whether she wished to die before me to avoid the pain of losing me.

At 87 years of age, Mum still lived in her own home with me and my brother (also unmarried and also aged over 60) and received the occasional five-minute phone call from her far-away daughters during the week. My brother and I have never been eloquent talkers so didn't interact with her much, and didn't go out much to socialise with others either, so we kept to ourselves. Sadly, that meant my mother spent most of her days doing household chores and endlessly watching TV to 'engage' with the world and keep her mind working. You could talk to her about any world news or current affairs. She was 'there' where the action was, despite not leaving the house, with the exception of those times when our healthier relatives turned up for lunches and dinners or to take her to the many medical specialists who kept her in one piece. She had accepted this as the way her life was meant to be since she had become a widow two decades earlier. She believed her quality of life was good despite the loneliness and the health complaints.

However, things changed that way of thinking when doctors treating my kidney cancer confirmed that it had progressed to stage 4: both Mum and I knew that it was a '*terminal*' illness.

The doctors offered me a course of last-line chemotherapy and I accepted it. I wasn't sure if I did it because I really wanted to stay alive or because I was afraid of dying. I went alone to the sessions and would not hear about anybody accompanying me. It was all too confronting to hear the words '*metastasis*', '*terminal*', '*palliative*', and see my body shrink and my hair go totally white in the space of a few weeks. That reality turned me initially into a grumpy, demanding patient and family member. And gradually, perhaps as acceptance of my prognosis set in, I seemed to transform into this sweet 'uncle'; a generous man with a big heart the family always knew I was, but who had been so elusive for decades.

It took my siblings several conversations to persuade me to put my affairs in order 'just in case of complications'. I reluctantly arranged my legal Will with the help of a lawyer and went a step further, formalising an advance care directive with my doctor before the time came when disease could leave me unable to make independent decisions. That was a relief to my family.

I nominated my sister as enduring guardian to decide on treatments for me at her discretion. I assumed she knew me well enough so I did not give her details of my care preferences. I just could not bring myself to discuss or imagine a time when I was not going to be in charge of myself. That was a cause of concern for my sister, but she avoided any confrontation as she knew I could not overcome my denial and she did not want to upset me further. I appreciated her thoughtfulness.

After the directive was out of the way, I felt I had been given a second chance at life and started to be more responsible and responsive; I joined in family gatherings and did not drink alcohol again – an overnight achievement. I did it so I could recover. Yes, I thought I would recover if I tried hard enough. Or at least I could fool the prognosis and remain alive for longer than anticipated. I felt it was never too late to start rebuilding my life, and there was no better time than when they told me my number was up. I put aside any statistics on the life expectancy of stage-4 cancer patients. In my mind, those numbers did not apply to me.

Being around me in the few months following the formalisation of the advance care directive has been heartening as many relatives did not know I had a clever sense of humour, a love of children, a tolerance of the unexpected, a high threshold for pain and infinite hope for survival. I have been making up for lost time while this body disintegrates. My family hardly recognise the '*new me*', but they act as if they know they are about to lose me.

As for my mother, she has become progressively more depressed even before I start to deteriorate, and our family has hopelessly witnessed her shrivel out of sight. Experts call this '*anticipatory grief*'.[5] In other words, preparing for the worst. Not her death, but mine. She has also chosen not to discuss the '*elephant in the room*'. Talks about last wishes, farewells, funerals or the 'D-word' (for death) are implicitly forbidden between the two of us. I know my sisters have arranged pre-paid funerals for both of us, but everybody has understood that avoidance is also Mum's very personal way of coping with bad news and that she does not need guidance or approval to remain silent on the matter. She only needs unconditional emotional support. She is still alive, her mind is still sharp, but her body is progressively getting frailer and a year after my terminal diagnosis, instead of calling the primary care doctor as the first point of contact she now visits the hospital every second month, every time she has a symptom, big or small. Maybe she has changed her mind about staying alive and regained her determination to get to 100 years of age and the hope of me living into my 80s.

I have also chosen not to discuss my future with any relatives and instead have decided to assume my life is going to be long. I ride my bicycle when I have to go to medical appointments and still don't allow any family members to come along to hear what the oncologist has to say about the next steps. It is my world, my news, my private feelings, and I do not want my autonomy taken away by other people's perspectives or my decision influenced by their fears or expectations. I refuse to hear any news on prognosis from anybody. My doctor knows I want to exercise my right to not know. As I see it, focusing on the inevitable is not the way to spend the rest of my life, however short it's going to be; after all, I've already exceeded my survival predictions!

The choice of facing and embracing or avoiding the truth about end-of-life is very personal and may have something to do with age, personality, life experience, culture and values; whatever it is, I believe it should be respected. My family tends to want to know more about my life expectancy, what my future symptoms will be when I approach the end, and treatments available as my disease progresses, but I, and many patients like me, want to know less to control our fear of death and to remain positive. I don't even use the word 'terminal'.

I have full mental capacity now, so want to keep a sense of control over this illness and over my life and choose to die in denial to not lose hope before my time comes. My choice is to not become an emotional burden on others by not sharing bad news; and to not indulge in self-pity. I know my family is not happy with this alienation from news about how my disease is progressing, but this is my life, my emotional baggage, and my right: to be in control of my privacy and die on my own terms. And if that is my idea of 'a good death' then this definition is what matters.

What do you think?

- What recommendations would you give to a terminally ill relative on how to prepare for death if there is no protocol?
- What is your opinion on clinicians agreeing not to tell patients the truth about prognosis if the patients do not want to hear it?
- How do you feel about the family being told about an impending death if the patient does not want to learn what is coming?

18

I think it was the right choice

The doorbell rang; it was my father's doctor. The home-care service sent a doctor once a week to manage his healthcare. This doctor was a decent, young professional, who at the outset appeared to be a new graduate. He was very focused and engaged in caring rather than prescribing unnecessary procedures. He had been taking care of my father for two years without skipping a week, not even during holidays. I remember calling him on a Saturday night once, in despair, after my father vomited blood. He answered promptly, calmed me down and sent an ambulance to take my father to hospital. To this day I remember overhearing music in the background during that call. He must have been in a restaurant with his family/wife/friends, but nevertheless he paused his social life to answer and reassure me. I was fortunate that I could count on a dedicated practitioner around my father.

It had been several years since the day when I received the call from my mother telling me that my father had been hospitalised with a brain bleed. She wasn't crying on the call, but by the tone of her voice I knew that his condition wasn't a minor ailment. The stroke condemned him to spending the rest of his life in bed with a breathing machine and a feeding tube. Weeks later he was discharged from hospital and brought back home thanks to a home-healthcare plan.

My parents' place was transformed into an improvised hospital in the home. What used to be our living room became my father's private ICU, an ICU inside our own house. Nurses, physiotherapists and other health workers came and went all the time, providing him with all manner of treatments. Some gave us hope of slight improvement in his condition, some treated him like another patient number; some were compassionate; others very business-like. Despite the many providers passing through the house, it was unclear to us who was leading the care, or whether there was any coordination among all those people. Nobody really explained why there was a plan to inflict all those treatments on my father when he probably was not even aware of it all. We did not know if he would have wanted that. As relatives, we felt as though my father had been abandoned in a sea of bureaucracy and health insurance bills, with no guidance. We all felt lost. The only constant emotional relief was the young doctor who came once a week.

In the beginning my mother coped with the situation, as she always had done during difficult periods in our lives. However, with this illness she saw my father going from 90 kg to less than 60 kg in a matter of weeks. His muscles vanished. We never knew why he became so thin even though he was being fed through his feeding tube six times a day. Ice cream had always been his favourite dessert and I think he missed it as for years he did not receive anything by mouth.

Before the stroke my father had had private health insurance. After the stroke we suddenly faced unexpected increases in out-of-pocket expenses for medications, rehabilitation, supplies, and the list went on. He was hospitalised more than usual, had more infections and also lost more weight. During all this time, I didn't see my mother cry. She found comfort in her religion and, even though she was uneducated, she understood that comfort care, not unnecessary suffering, was in my father's best interest. She was capable of searching for information on ways to stop painful procedures being carried out on him.

Then, nine years after my father's stroke and two weeks after their 35th wedding anniversary, I arrived home to find my mother had collapsed on the kitchen floor. I took her to hospital, incidentally the same one my father had been taken to when he had had his stroke. The doctors called me the next day for a family conference. I went there alone, as we didn't have any other relatives, only neighbours. Ovarian cancer with metastasis in her liver, lungs and bones was what the specialists announced at the meeting. Her condition was even worse than my father's, and emergency surgery was proposed. I was in shock, so I agreed to the procedure without fully understanding the reasons, benefits or harms. She died two days after the surgery from complications. According to some doctors, routine screening for other age-appropriate conditions, or simply an annual general check-up, might have uncovered some signs of the cancer earlier and, who knows, might even have prevented the cancer from spreading the way it had – routine check-ups that I know my mother stopped having as she was so busy being a dedicated carer.

The young, focused doctor had been excellent at managing my father and our emotional wellbeing, but he had unintentionally overlooked the fact that my elderly mother was probably burdened as a carer to a point of self-neglect. That had not occurred to me either. Her health was off our radar. We had both missed that over the years. She was such a stoic heroine, she had never complained.

My mother did not have enough time to alleviate my father's suffering through to the end. I remember that 'palliative care' was proposed by my father's last specialist weeks before my mother had that catastrophic fatal episode. I did not give it enough attention at that time, but now that my mother was not there I was able to accept the idea and consider this option for him. I would not let my father suffer anymore.

The palliative care journey commenced. No more needles, no more antibiotics, no more painful procedures – only oral pain medication and some soup and ice cream through the tube. That hospital-like environment changed; medical papers on the wall were replaced with family photos. Within days his wellbeing was restored: by that I mean he passed away shortly after my mother died. I am still mourning both of them, but the thought that comforts me is that I think I made the right choice by him.

What do you think?

- Do you know someone who spends most of his/her days caring for a frail family member? When would be a good time to ask them how they are coping?
- Would it be intrusive or beneficial for home care services to be aware of all relevant people in the household who cannot access care?
- Who do you think might object to this?

19

Dying and grieving during pandemic lockdown

Mum was looking forward to visiting me, her youngest son, in Spain during the summer holidays of 2018. She had celebrated her 60th birthday a couple of months before and had never travelled out of her own country, so this was going to be a great adventure. I had moved to Spain for a temporary job and found love and permanent residency so she wanted to witness my newly found happiness and be part of my new life. She had her first passport issued and purchased her ticket, then went for a routine medical check-up to get travel insurance before the six-week holiday. At the doctor's she was told she had a growing mass in her abdomen that needed immediate attention and that she had to put her holiday on hold.

The following weeks were packed with tests and many specialist appointments until she finally was told the verdict: stage 4 colon cancer with liver metastasis. She would have to cancel her plans to leave the country and concentrate on saving her life through major surgery and chemotherapy. It was so awful for all of us and it all happened too quickly. However, I remember after the initial shock she was very positive and determined to beat her prognosis by surviving beyond what the mortality statistics predicted for her.

So she embarked on her first major surgery, which went well, and seven months later I had an opportunity to visit her back home before she started her first course of chemotherapy. I wanted to see her before those aggressive drugs changed her appearance and quenched her boundless energy. I wanted to remember her the youthful way she always was and have long talks before her brain was affected by the treatment or the illness. We spent a wonderful couple of months together sharing what we could between her chemotherapy and follow-up appointments. Even though the drugs made her sick, she was willing to go out and reminisce at the places we used to go during my younger years.

Before I emigrated to Spain we had adopted a cat which I couldn't take with me when I left the country, so I had left Mum in charge of her. The cat became her daughter, and was an inseparable companion; it made her laugh, they slept together, they played and my mother often spoiled it by giving it its favourite treats. There was such a profound connection between my mother and the cat that when she returned from spending a few days in hospital, the cat received her effusively, and the following days they spent many hours together.

For the ensuing months Mum endured multiple surgeries for recurrent tumours, laboratory testing, specialist consultations and changes of therapies, including a trial of biological agents. She did not want to give up, no matter how much those aggressive treatments affected her quality and enjoyment of life. She was so young and had so much to live for: us, her immediate family.

Mum had been a very hard-working person who cared about us and constantly instilled in us the love for studying, and that's why she always gave us her full support when we considered moving away to follow our careers. She was a health worker who opened her own consulting room at my grandmother's house, where she always went after finishing her morning shift at a company. We lived near Grandma's house, so Mum always enjoyed the walk there. During her last months she told me that cancer had taken away her feet and a few years of life, so she was deprived of doing what she liked best: walking and going wherever she wanted and managing her own affairs without depending on anyone.

After eight months of her first chemotherapy round, she felt strong enough and the tests indicated her body was responding to treatment so doctors agreed she was fit enough to travel. In 2019 she was able to realise her dream of travelling to Spain and meeting my girlfriend; the experience was enhanced by having my father and brother join our tours to Portugal, Italy and France. We almost forgot her diagnosis and made the most of each day together. During those six weeks we laughed and ate like there was no tomorrow. Perhaps because there was no tomorrow.

In order to make her trip to Europe, my mum had had to leave the cat alone at home, but she had arranged for her sister-in-law to come and be with it every day. While she was in the middle of the trip, we received a call from the sister-in-law saying that the cat had disappeared. She had already searched for it throughout the apartment and had been unable to find it. Mum's home was on the fourth floor of an apartment block and when her sister-in-law looked out from the balcony she noticed something in the garden. She rushed down and found the cat hidden in the bushes and very scared. Luckily it had suffered no harm when falling from such a height. That news for my mum was very reassuring. The cat was her precious companion.

During the two years she spent fighting cancer, my mum and I sent each other messages via Instagram. I always shared a photo of cute or funny cats with her; I sent her these because I felt that when I showed them to her, for a moment she forgot about the illness that was consuming her.

Sometimes I did not realise the severity of her disease. Distance is a barrier that does not let you see reality, despite the fact that my father, who is a doctor, told me the prognosis was days of life – perhaps weeks. I think that denial was my coping mechanism against the fear of the imminent death of such an important person in my life.

Then in February 2020 the doctors told us her body was no longer responding to the biological agents and medical science could not offer her anything else to prolong her life. At that point, the doctors' recommendation for Mum was for all active treatments to be suspended. They offered her the option of palliative care in a hospice, but she decided against it. She wanted to die peacefully at home and with the people she loved, in an environment where she felt safe. She distrusted the treatment she was going to receive and thought the hospice was very cold and isolating. She did not put it in writing in a formal advance care directive, but she discussed details of her wishes with the treating team, and with Dad. 'I'm afraid this is going to be your job,' she told him. 'I want to be at home until the end.'

By this time COVID-19 had become a familiar term outside China. This pandemic had spread through the entire world, but Spain, where I currently live, was hit particularly hard and we were in a very strict lockdown. Patients who went into hospital had to say their goodbyes before admission as visitors were not allowed, to prevent the risk of further infection. Some patients were monitored through glass walls without the touch of a doctor, and nurses updated families by phone or video call. Dying in hospital during the pandemic was a new, ghastly experience for everyone, where the virus robbed families of the last chance to accompany their loved ones who might be afraid to go alone. But health restrictions were non-negotiable and relatives had no choice. I too had no choice but to remain in lockdown as international borders were closed. Grieving in absentia, before and after death, became a new global concept.

Mum's 62nd birthday came a few weeks later, and while we were all relieved she had made it, she was very frail and had lost too much weight and her appetite so the family did not go out.

She had a modest celebration of cake and carnival masks with her immediate family in the dining room of her home and I joined via video call from Spain. Being a helpless spectator through video calls in moments like that marks one's life. I never thought I was going to experience this situation. We had no idea she had five weeks left to live.

My life changed a lot. I always worried about contacting my mum through video calls because it was very hard for me to see on my mobile phone that her state of health was worsening every day. In a matter of 10-12 days, her last days, her health fell into a tailspin and we could no longer have a meaningful or uninterrupted conversation. She was no longer expressing herself as before. Everything happened very fast; I was hoping to travel as soon as possible to see her for the last time, and give her a tight hug, like the first time I went to visit her after learning that she had cancer. But as fate had it, coronavirus deprived me of my right.

Despite what was happening, my dad had a positive frame of mind; he said that pandemic lockdown was the best situation Mum could have gone through, because she was at peace, with no people around seeing her or crying. The day my mum passed away, the cat lay on her legs and spent time with her. It comforts me a little to think that final touch was what Mum would have wanted.

However, for us, the survivors, it was a different process. Being unable to attend her funeral and pay tribute to her life in front of a multitude of people, whom she had touched and who loved her, was the last straw for me. It was lonely and devastating. It was unfair. She deserved better, even after death. Instead we had a virtual memorial with family and friends from five countries. It was a consolation since we can't predict when we will see each other again.

Mourning under the current situation locked up at home (working at home/restricted home life, no freedom to go out and debrief) has, of course, made the loss of Mum so much harder to endure. Grief has completely changed my routine because, before, we talked every day for hours despite the time difference. Now that she's gone, I think of her often and have trouble finding other things to keep myself busy while in lockdown.

I will remember her courage in facing so much medical intervention; for making it clear to all of us that she wanted all available treatment done until there was no more hope; for trying hard to be with us one more month, one more week, despite her own suffering; for giving us the satisfaction of being with her in one way or another, physically and virtually, while ending her days at a place of her choice: her own home.

What do you think?

- Why do you think most people prefer to die at home? Does location matter to you? Why is that?
- Have you known anybody who had to die alone in a hospital because of pandemic restrictions? Why is it a good or bad idea for health institutions to relax visiting restrictions for families of people who are dying during a pandemic?

20

Dad, sorry we can't honour your wishes

Martin was in his early 70s when he was diagnosed with dementia. He had lost his wife 15 years earlier and had nursed her at home up until the last month before her death. He had loved his wife dearly and would often speak fondly about caring for her at home and, although tough at times, he never spoke of these struggles to his children. He would often say how he had never wanted his wife in a nursing home and that he believed it had been his responsibility to care for her. In keeping with this, he had expressed his wish over the years to his children that he never wanted himself to be '*sent away*' to a nursing home.

Martin's two adult daughters lived close by and would visit him weekly, bringing the groceries, a newspaper and entertaining gossip about their families. Before his formal diagnosis of dementia, his daughters had noticed subtle changes in their father. He would often forget appointments and important dates, and at times they would notice his mood fluctuate between withdrawing from family conversation to becoming easily agitated with friends and family. It was all out of character for him and distressing for his relatives. His loving and caring personality was fading away; no longer could he joke, or relate to the grandchildren in meaningful ways. The young ones were the first to be forgotten.

After investigation by medical teams and the words *'Alzheimer's disease'* had finally been pronounced, Martin's two daughters were confronted with the need to seriously change their lifestyle and arranged between them to visit their father more regularly and to assist with shopping, appointments and day-to-day activities.

This plan worked well for the family for the first few months after diagnosis. Martin's daughters felt he was managing well and they were positive that the early treatment offered by his doctor was helping. As time went on, though, the family noticed that Martin might not have been coping as well as they had thought. Meals that had been prepared earlier were often left untouched; they would often find him wearing the same clothes for days on end, and he was becoming more frustrated at their insistence on arranging extra support for him at home. They noticed his memory was becoming more impaired and felt he needed more support at home, which they were not able to provide.

Adjustments were happening progressively as both daughters were trying to juggle their father's everyday needs as well as caring for their own young children and satisfying the other responsibilities of their paid jobs. Eventually, Martin agreed for healthcare workers and community assistants to visit his home and, although these services were not provided daily, the daughters felt their father was better off with this added support.

As time went on it became more and more obvious that Martin needed further supervision. He had become frailer and was falling over as he wanted to keep active but would often forget his walking stick. While he had not had any serious injuries, the family was aware it was only a matter of time. His doctor was becoming more concerned with Martin's ability to care for himself and discussed with the family possible admission into residential care where he would have 24-hour supervision. Both daughters were aware of their father's position on this and refused to *'send him away',* so they insisted on caring for him at his home for more hours a week. This added stress and arguments between them due to their father's demands and need for round-the-clock assistance.

One afternoon, when one of the daughters came to Martin's house after picking the children up from school at the end of a day's work, she found her father on the kitchen floor where he had been since the early hours. He had not been able to get up to reach a phone or remember a phone number to call for help.

'It looks like it's no longer safe to keep Dad here alone,' she realised. He had quietly stopped taking his regular lunchtime medications, which had contributed to the fall which this time landed him in hospital.

On admission to hospital the family was told of '*respite care*' as a trial as this would give the daughters some time to recharge their batteries, but they felt guilty; they had known his wishes of never being '*sent away*'.

'I'm prepared to leave my part-time job to care for Dad at home,' said the daughter most highly affected by feelings of guilt. 'I feel we have let him down already. If we send him to respite care, then next thing is we'll agree to keep him permanently in care, away from us. If he could tell us, he would say he hated that idea.'

The nearby nursing home facility staff held a discussion with the family regarding the amount of care and resources Martin would need day and night. It was clear going to his former home was not feasible and a joint decision was made to trial respite for him. This was another adaptation challenge for all, but after a couple of weeks in respite Martin's daughter was so upset that he was institutionalised and not in a family home she chose to bring her father to live with her family.

Martin's confusion about his changes of environment put his health at risk despite all efforts made by the daughter to adjust the home safely for him. He would wander at night, turning electrical appliances on and trying to open doors to get out, and at times slept on the floor or in the lounge, disoriented and not knowing how to get back to his new bedroom.

The close supervision and demanding number of tasks he required assistance with affected the daughter's family dynamics and quality time as she was constantly exhausted and often moody. She felt she was honouring her father's wishes but also felt incompetent and unhappy. Painful as it was, she came to the realisation that her father was not receiving optimal care in her house and deserved better, so this arrangement only lasted a short time and the original decision of outsourcing Martin's care to a nursing home facility had to be brought up again in conversation.

The daughters went through online catalogues of services and considered the distance from home, levels of care offered, green surroundings, exercise programs, food quality and staff skills of several nursing homes in the area. An aged-care facility was eventually chosen for Martin that both daughters were pleased with, and he transitioned into this new environment relatively well, except for the harrowing first few visits where he would get ready to go home with his daughters when they started indicating they were leaving for the day. His questions about going home diminished after a few visits, to everyone's relief. Despite his illness worsening, he remained settled and his children and grandchildren visited regularly, helping him regain the quality of life he had lost, even if he was unaware of it.

While they were painfully aware they had not honoured their father's wishes, these were no longer relevant if he could not be safely cared for in an appropriate setting, and home was no longer that place. After witnessing their father being supported by staff and volunteers, and recovering their own family harmony, the guilt slowly lessened as they felt their father's life situation had improved since his move to a home where he received appropriate care, was involved in closely monitored activities, and socialised with other residents to the extent that he could.

Martin survived several years in this care facility and peacefully died from natural causes at the age of 78, surrounded by his loving daughters and supportive staff.

What do you think?

- What is your perspective on placing older people in institutions if, as in the case of the father in this story, the person's wishes are no longer relevant because what was once thought possible isn't anymore?
- How confident are you about knowing your parents' or grandparents' views on what is an acceptable place of care in their last years of life?

21

The future me

'How could the "*now me*" make health decisions for the "*future me*"?' Grace asked earnestly, searching my eyes. Her indigenous ancestry presented me with a new perspective on '*time*' that did not conceive of past, present and future in a single irrevocable linear direction, measured in units of different size and with their values assigned by Western society.[6]

I was silent, willing her to say more, to help me understand her reticence in completing the advance care planning document the medical team had entrusted me to deliver, as the senior clinical nurse in a Western health system. To people of her culture, '*time*' was a series of life events revolving around the person like an aura with, not a chronological, but a relevance focus.[6] This meant the word 'advance' was probably a big hurdle in our communication.

I was struck by the difference in language between the healthcare team and the family of this quietly suffering woman. The physician needed her to understand three things: the limits of what the hospital could provide; that medical interventions were no long on offer; and that her prognosis was bleak. Were we too late in communicating this? Perhaps, or perhaps not. Because to Grace and her family, the concentric distribution of '*time*' events around the person was based on a very personal ranking of importance that represented the priorities of the individual in a community at a given point,[6] perhaps there was hope we could still get our message across – the message that having a written statement of choices and plan of care would facilitate decisions and be a deciding factor in what management Grace would receive when the '*time*' came.

Our limited understanding of this very important notion of 'time' becomes clearer if we think about how the Western world perceives the idea of patient-centred care: shared healthcare decisions that converge around the specific physical and psychosocial needs of an individual, and their delivery in partnership and alignment with the patient's preferences and values.[7] Yet, Grace's family was not even starting with 'Mum, we're worried you are getting sicker by the day and we haven't talked about... ' or 'Auntie, before we run out of time, can we chat about what you'd like doctors to do for you? Or what treatments you'd prefer them to stop?' It was as if there was no need for any direct exchange of words. We, the healthcare team, could not grapple with how implicit their communication was, or envisage how they would come around to making decisions – either Grace herself as the patient, or her relatives as a clan – if she were to experience a critical health complication.

Grace spoke of the lengths her family had gone to – accommodating her losses of role and function; accepting her inability to return home to her country; being willing to fly to the city at an expense far beyond their means – all to honour her and offer her peace and emotional healing.

'What are we to do?' I asked her. 'Do you know what your doctors want of you and why?'

'Yes, of course,' she replied graciously. 'They need me to say I do not want to be resuscitated. Maybe my daughter knows this; but my husband, my son, no.'

'Is there anything you would be willing to do or say to the doctors, without giving up anything of value to you?' I asked. I was hoping for compromise so that Grace would receive the most appropriate care; so that the community palliative care team could support her and her ever-expanding family in her sister's suburban home.

Chapter 21

'I would consent to my daughter, Bella, making decisions on my behalf, if I was too sick to speak for myself. She knows me; we know each other. She knows what is important to me; I trust her completely and always.'

Fat tears ran uninterrupted down Bella's face, dripping from her chin onto Grace's passive foot. I could not work out if she was overwhelmed by the responsibility of the role suddenly entrusted to her, or whether they were tears of pride and resignation to the cultural privilege of being someone's advocate and surrogate decision-maker.

'Bella,' I ventured, 'Would you accept this role?'

My question made both women laugh.

'Of course,' Bella stated, as if talking to a person with hearing loss. 'That is our way.'

It was an unspoken cultural tradition that did not need to be formalised because '*time*' for them was either a static 'living in the now' or a fluid concept where events from the past and present were entangled and the important issue was not when, but what happened.[6]

The right hand of each woman sought the other's. Bella's left hand rested protectively on her rounded abdomen. No more words were needed. I left the intimacy of the curtained medical ward cubicle and made my retreat.

Grace died in her sister's home a month later with the support of her deeply-grieving family and the palliative care community team to help manage her ravaging symptoms.

Grace's beliefs came from her indigenous spirituality which sustained her sense of self, status and purpose. She had no intention of formalising any paperwork, and neither did her daughter. The clash between Grace's worldview and that of the mainstream healthcare model was irreconcilable. However, although she didn't sign any documents, a workable compromise was reached by Grace openly nominating a surrogate decision-maker, a role that was implicit in her culture.

She and her love-filled daughter have inspired and instructed my practice and left me with two legacies: the new (to me) concept of non-linear time, and the idea of 'the future me'.

What do you think?

- What do you think 'the future you' might choose differently in terms of treatments and place of death to what your preferences are today?
- What would make you formalise an advance care directive for future critical illness? Who would you nominate to take the role of decision-maker on your behalf and why?

22

The 'other' end of end-of-life

I've seen someone die.

That's not a remarkable achievement in itself, but it's also not something a lot of 15-year-olds can say. Then again, most 15-year-olds don't aspire to become funeral directors.

Having observed the stages of death as defined by morticians – respiratory and cardiac arrest, cessation of neuronal function, pallor mortis – eventually proved helpful during my mortuary training three years later. However, people often forget that death isn't just an event – it's a process, and one that can start long before the heart stops beating.

When my grandmother neared the end of that process, unconscious in a tiny, overwhelmingly beige hospital room after a stroke, I knew I had to be there for her. Having been absent for the death of my grandpa 18 months earlier, I couldn't stand the thought of my frail 'Nanna' flat-lining alone in the darkened ward. So Dad and I made the trek up to sit with her, to whisper comforting words and to hold her hand one last time, stroking her tissue-papery fingers until they went limp. We were the only ones there when she died; her daughters were stuck in traffic 10 minutes away when we called to give them the news.

The guilt that comes from not being there for someone when they need you is unlike any other – it sticks around for a long time and flares up when you least expect it. Grandpa, who was not particularly ill, just old, had come over for dinner the week before he died, and I'd barely spoken to him, claiming I was 'too busy'. He was mourning the passing of a close friend from his youth a few days before, and it seemed to me that anything I, his youngest grandchild, could say about his loss would only make it awkward, so I remained silent and concentrated on my cooking to make him more comfortable. I hadn't yet been trained for that kind of talk, so after serving him I 'escaped' to my bedroom to study.

As a trainee mortician, at the age of 18, I liked the clinical aspects of the work – the autopsies, the embalming, making people look nice for the last time anyone might see them – but not so much the social, emotional part. I was more concerned about the bodies than the people, which, retrospectively, is an unhelpful approach. The dead person on my slab didn't care about the quality of my conversation, but the live grandfather in my kitchen most probably did. I denied him that.

Mortuary training includes speaking sensitively to the bereaved, which I think is far easier than speaking to those anticipating a death. When the inevitable happens, people have their memories to hang on to. Morticians hear those descriptions, which help them make a picture of who the deceased was, what they treasured, what they achieved, what they feared and who loved them. They don't have to 'fix' anything or perform a miracle to save their clients' lives. Morticians don't have to explain to families that science can't help them keep their loved one alive. They just have to replicate a dignifying picture of how the deceased was perceived by other people, and imprint that memory to last forever in their family's minds.

I'm not so successful, or even marginally skilful, when it comes to living people. Even now, every time I cancel plans in favour of studying, I remember poor Grandpa picking at the gourmet dinner with the expensive varieties of cheese I had baked for him, while I immersed myself in exam notes at the other end of the house. His last supper with us and he didn't even eat, probably thinking about his dead friend or even having more mundane thoughts of the plain baked potatoes and apple pie back at his place. Looking back over five years later, that exam was a blip in my school career – I don't even remember what it was on or what marks I got – but I know I'd have happily accepted a low mark if it had meant one last game of Scrabble or darts with Grandpa, one last discussion on gardening advice, one last time hearing about the adventures he had had in his assorted career paths. Had I known that would be the last time I'd ever see him, I'd have taken the opportunity to absorb another fragment of his worldly wisdom.

But how could I have known? People talk about living each day to the fullest, because it could be our last. Or theirs. That's not something people my age tend to think about. We assume we're invincible for at least the next 50 years.

I'd initially gone into mortuary science because I thought it would help with my ultimate dream of studying medicine, not really reflecting that most work in healthcare is concerned with the 'before' part of the end-of-life process rather than the 'after'. I figured I had many years of training to master the final conversation, but I never imagined how soon it would happen, or how helpless and guilty I would feel when it did in my first placement during my first year. It's a lot harder when you know about the details of life behind the death. You can't separate the baggage and the richness and just look at the aftermath of the event as working material. There are incredible stories of joy and sorrow that need to be cherished long before the funeral.

The first year of my medical training was mostly online due to pandemic restrictions, and the joy and empowerment that comes from helping others was largely replaced by vulnerability and insecurity in my healthcare skills.[8] There were changes to the way people in residential aged care were managed and isolated for their own protection during the pandemic, and the protocol for hospital-admitted patients implied they generally had to die removed from their families. I can't begin to imagine going through that, but realised that if my grandfather had been alive at the time of the pandemic he would probably have had a similar experience. This made it difficult for me to see it happen to others. Even funerals had restrictions to number of attendees. The uncertainty surrounding how long this pandemic would last meant the entire culture of preparing for death and supporting the aftermath was a luxury the health system couldn't afford, and, having dreamed of my career as the best way to help people, I wasn't expecting to be an unskilled bystander when something historical like that was taking place.

Consequently, I leapt at the first opportunity I received to get some hands-on experience – a placement offered by one of my teachers, who was a GP at a nearby clinic. As a young, naïve student, I liked the idea of working in general practice rather than hospitals – enjoyable, varied and low stakes. Or so I thought. So, I set off with my crisp new white coat and a diploma that proved I knew how to work with people who were already dead. Surely, no experiences with the living could be worse than that. It turned out there's a reason why becoming a doctor takes so many years. It is much harder to deal with the living.

One patient has stuck with me the most out of everyone I saw that day. Alana was in her mid-40s, but she'd already had years of chemotherapy and two surgeries for a cancer that had spread to three organs. Even as a first-year student, I could already tell that wasn't going to end well, but it was going to end soon. She'd come to Dr Kramer for the first time that day because of his expertise in natural and nutritional treatments. She was having a miserable time with chemotherapy and other treatments which left her with debilitating pain and nausea, so she wanted to learn about other options that might meaningfully extend her life without reducing its quality. I think Dr Kramer and I both knew that not only was there very little that could help her at this point, but also that her brain didn't seem to have registered this fact. Surely, the specialists had already told her?

Watching from the corner of the office as this young woman essentially pleaded for her life, only to receive suggestions of potential natural placebos in return, made me wonder if perhaps, even with all his years of experience, Dr Kramer was also uncomfortable confronting Alana with the truth of her prognosis. I couldn't blame him. Or perhaps I didn't understand that he was actually very confidently using a compassionate care strategy. The straightforward, albeit socially inept, mortician in me wanted to just be direct and tell Alana that no amount of herbal tea or vitamin infusions would be likely to significantly delay her death, but as a student I knew that wasn't my place. Not that I'm insensitive, I just didn't want her to waste any minute of her very limited time on futile management. However, if I put on my relative's hat, I knew I could never have said that to either of my grandparents, even if they were much older and had subconsciously expected to reach the end of their natural lives any day. Still, it was difficult to just sit there and let it happen. I'd thought I was there to help.

However, when I saw how Alana lit up at the idea that becoming a vegan might make a difference, I realised that Dr Kramer might have more of a plan than I had given him credit for. What Alana probably needed most was palliative care, but after speaking to her for an hour I figured that destroying her last shred of hope might just do more damage than placebo treatments. These actions are called '*supportive care*' and include psychosocial and spiritual nurturing, not only about the day-by-day of the current illness but also about their family's preparation for bereavement. It also involves patients setting limits on what they want to know, and clinicians respecting these boundaries and refraining from being too outspoken.

Having spent some time around healthcare workers during this first year of my medical training, I knew part of our job was to make life better, or at least more bearable, within the disability that illnesses impose on our patients. If that involved a cure, great! But if some preferred to hear that a cup of tea was just as effective against their terminal illness as futile medication, then maybe that belief should be respected. Stopping Alana's treatment wouldn't kill her faster, but continuing it might, and even though I'd only met her that afternoon, I wanted her last days to be filled with some gratification and emotional support, and not spent alone in bed in an institution.

Patients do have the right to know what's going to happen to them, but they also have a right not to. And clinicians don't have the right to take away their hope if that keeps them feeling alive.

I still dream of using my mortician skills to make families feel better 'after' the inevitable happens, while I contribute as a [future] doctor in the 'before', trying to prevent or postpone the end. Everything I've done throughout the course of my first stage of tertiary education has been with the intention of providing people with the dignified care they deserve – both before and after death. Funerals are as much for the living as they are for the dead, but so is the rest of the process before the actual passing. Everyone has different reasons for making the choices they do in such difficult situations; there isn't one right way to approach the end of life, but it should always be centred around the needs and wishes of the patient. We owe them that. You can't always know when that process is going to start or end, so, take it from an undertaker: consider whether you want to know, but live like you're already halfway there.

What do you think?

- If you had only months or weeks to live, how much detail would you like to know?
- Do you know someone who was grateful for their doctor's honesty in giving them bad news on prognosis? What do you think are the benefits and harms of truth disclosure?
- Is the aftermath care as important to you as the time leading to a loved one's death? What is your reason for your view?
- How early should medical students and other health trainees be coached about breaking bad news?

Afterword: where to from here?

Norman Swan

When we're healthy and well, it's hard to imagine that something bad can happen to us at any time: a diagnosis of cancer, a car crash, a stroke. We might be unaware of what's occurred but our families have to deal with the aftermath and decide on our behalf what should happen next: another round of chemo, prolonged ventilation, tube feeding, another operation or intravenous antibiotics.

The evidence is that all too much is done to us when it's known that death is imminent and that if we'd been able to be asked, we'd have refused. Pity the poor children or spouses who are left to wonder and argue over what their father/mother/wife/husband/brother/sister would have really wanted. The personal costs to families and the economic costs to the nation are huge.

The stories you've just read in this book should inspire you to start having critical conversations in your family about each other's wishes at the end of life, when care might be futile, painful and even perhaps life shortening. It's been shown in some research that appropriate palliative care can in fact extend life and better quality life at that. Then document what you've agreed and make sure everyone knows about it, including your GP. If you're a GP reading this, again the evidence suggests that your patients want you to bring this up, yet only a small percentage of you do.

Death is part of life and it should be as good as life, not the horror that it can be, needlessly, if we'd only planned ahead.

Norman Swan

Renowned multi-award-winning producer recognised in Australia for his work on *Health Minutes* and the radio program *Health Report*, and known internationally for his work for the American Medical Association and the World Health Organization. He is a medically qualified radio and TV health journalist with many years' experience in researching and broadcasting health issues and their associated physiological, environmental and social causes and consequences. Go to *A better death* at:

www.abc.net.au/radionational/programs/healthreport/a-better-death/7254660

Resources

References

Chapter 1: Grandma

1. https://www.dyingmatters.org/page/updated-resources

Chapter 3: An unexpected friendship

2. End PJ paralysis movement. https://endpjparalysis.org/

Chapter 8: The 'daughter from California' syndrome

3. Mollow DW, Clarnette RM, Braun EA, *et al.* Decision making in the incompetent elderly: "The Daughter from California syndrome". *J Am Geriatr Soc.* 1991;39(4): 396-399. DOI: 10.1111/j.1532-5415.1991.tb02907.x

Chapter 15: A celebration of life on his own terms

4. Burton L. Recovering from caregiver stress and burnout. *High Speed Training* 29 August 2018. www.highspeedtraining.co.uk/hub/caregiver-stress-and-burnout/

Chapter 17: The right not to know

5. Coelho A, Barbosa A. Family anticipatory grief: An integrative literature review. *Am J Hosp Pall Care* 2017; 34(8): 774-785. DOI: 10.1177/1049909116647960

Chapter 21: The future me

6. Janca A, Bullen, C. The Aboriginal Concept of Time and its Mental Health Implications. *Australasian Psychiatry* 2003; 11(1_suppl): S40–S44. https://doi.org/10.1046/j.1038-5282.2003.02009.x

7. NEJM Catalyst. What is patient-centered care? *NEJM Catalyst: Innovations in Care Delivery* 1 January 2017. https://catalyst.nejm.org/doi/full/10.1056/CAT.17.0559

Chapter 22: The 'other' end of end-of-life

8. Ross SB, Kumar M, Dillon A, Bahudin D, Cardona M. COVID-19 impact on medical education and the future post-pandemic era for medical students. *British Student Doctor Journal* 2020; 4(2): 54-59. http://doi.org/10.18573/bsdj.170

Further relevant reading

International publications

Cardona M, Anstey M, Lewis E, et al. Appropriateness of intensive care treatments near the end of life during the COVID-19 pandemic. *Breathe* 2020; 16; 200062. DOI: 10.1183/20734735.0062-2020

Cardona M, Kellett J, Lewis E, Brabrand M, Ni Chroinin D. Truth disclosure on prognosis: Is it ethical not to communicate personalised risk of death? *Int Journal of Clinical Practice* 2018; 72(8): e13222. https://onlinelibrary.wiley.com/doi/abs/10.1111/ijcp.13222

Gristina GR1, De Gaudio R, Mazzon D, Curtis JR. End of life care in Italian intensive care units: where are we now? *Minerva Anestesiol* 2011 ; 77(9): 911-920.

Lewis ET, Harrison R, Hanly L, Psirides A, et al. End-of-life priorities of older adults with terminal illness and caregivers: qualitative consultation. *Health Expectations* 2019; 22(3): 405-414. https://onlinelibrary.wiley.com/doi/full/10.1111/hex.12860

Li LB. Ethics and end-of-life care for critically ill patients in China. Clinical review. *Critical Care* 2013; 17 17(6): 244. www.ncbi.nlm.nih.gov/pmc/articles/PMC4057346/

Mani RK, Amin P, Chawla R, Divatia JV, et al. Guidelines for end-of-life and palliative care in Indian intensive care units: ISCCM consensus Ethical Position Statement. *Indian J Crit Care Med* 2012; 16(3): 166-181.

McGrath P, Holewa H. Seven Principles for Indigenous Palliative Care Service Delivery: Research Findings from Australia. *AustralAsian Journal of Cancer* 2006; 5(3): 179-186.

Olarte JMN, Guillen DG. Cultural Issues and Ethical Dilemmas in Palliative and End-of-Life Care in Spain. *Cancer Control* 2001; 8(1). http://www.medscape.com/viewarticle/409033

Pennec S, Monnier A, Pontone S, Aubry R. End-of-life medical decisions in France: a death certificate follow-up survey 5 years after the 2005 act of parlia- ment on patients' rights and end of life. *BMC Palliative Care* 2012; 11: 25. https://bmcpalliatcare.biomedcentral.com/articles/10.1186/1472-684X-11-25

Skulason B, Hauksdottir A, Ahcic K, Helg AR. Death talk: gender differences in talking about one's own impending death. *BMC Palliative Care* 2014; 13: 8.

Soares M. End of life care in Brazil: the long and winding road. *Critical Care* 2011; 15(1): 110. doi: 10.1186/cc9962.

Steinhauser KE1, Clipp EC, Mc- Neilly M, Christakis NA, McIntyre LM, Tulsky JA. In search of a good death: observations of patients, families, and providers. *Ann Intern Med* 2000; 132(10): 825-832.

Tan A, MancaD. Finding common ground to achieve a "good death": family physicians working with substitute decision-makers of dying patients. A qualitative grounded theory study. *BMC Family Practice* 2013; 14:14.

Wilson ME, Dobler CC, Zubek L, Gajic O, et al. Prevalence of disagreement about appropriateness of treatment between ICU patients/surrogates and clinicians. *Chest* 2019; 155(6): 1140-1147. https://pubmed.ncbi.nlm.nih.gov/30922949/

UK and Ireland resources

Planning ahead for the end of life
> NHS Choices, UK
> www.nhs.uk/Planners/end-of-life-care/Pages/planning

Fill in the Think Ahead Form (Ireland) https://hospicefoundation.ie/programmes/public-awareness/think-ahead/fill-in-think-ahead-form/

Healthcare Improvement Scotland – Anticipatory Care Planning Toolkit: Let's think ahead
> https://ihub.scot/project-toolkits/anticipatory-care-planning

Resources

Janette Barrie, from NHS Lanarkshire, discusses Anticipatory Care
   Planning (blog) 22nd July 2016
   www.qnis.org.uk/blog/anticipatory-care-planning
Good Life, Good Death, Good Grief: Scottish compassionate
   communities toolkit
   www.goodlifedeathgrief.org.uk/content/toolkit_homepage/
Death and bereavement
   NHSinform
   www.nhsinform.scot/care-support-and-rights/death-and-
   bereavement
Advance Care Plan
   Byw Nawr
   http://advancecareplan.org.uk/advance-care-planning
Advance Care Planning
   Compassion in Dying
   https://compassionindying.org.uk/making-decisions-and-planning
Planning your care in advance
   Marie Curie UK
   www.mariecurie.org.uk/help/support/terminal-illness/planning
Planning now for your future – Advance Care Planning
   Dementia UK
   www.dementiauk.org/get-support/legal-and-financial-
   information/advance-care-planning
Dr Rammya Mathew
   Death and dying needs greater public health focus (blog)
   22 April 2016
   www.dyingmatters.org/blog/DeathAndDyingneedsgreater
   publichealthfocus
NHS End of Life Care
   www.england.nhs.uk/eolc/
Think Ahead: Planning for Dying, Death and Care
   The Irish Hospice Foundation
   https://hospicefoundation.ie/programmes/public-awareness/
   think-ahead/
The Irish Cancer Society – Palliative Care
   www.cancer.ie
Ann Twomey: We Need to Talk about Dementia and Palliative Care (blog)
   28th April 2020
   https://pallcare4dementia.com/6-we-need-to-talk-about-dementia

Advance care planning in Northern Ireland
Macmillan Cancer Support
www.macmillan.org.uk/information-and-support/oesophageal-
gullet-cancer
Diane Walker – Annie's story: an example of advance care planning in
action (blog) 8th February 2017
https://gmcuk.wordpress.com/2017/02/08/annies-story-an-
example-of-advance-care-planning
Advance & Future Care Plans
NHS Wales
www.wales.nhs.uk/researchandresources/publications/
nhswalesadvancefuturecareplans
Death Cafe United Kingdom
https://deathcafe.com/c/United_Kingdom/
Message in a Bottle
http://lionsgiving.co.uk/national-appeals/message-in-a-bottle
Talking about advance care planning (YouTube)
General Medical Council
www.youtube.com/watch?v=jEuSm-XY3Ms
Byw Nawr: What is the difference between 'advance care planning' and an
'advance care plan'? (YouTube)
www.youtube.com/watch?v=lMjuX2_9Qyg

Australian resources

Advance Care Planning Australia
www.advancecareplanning.org.au/contact-us
Advance Care Planning for Healthy Dying
Tasmanian Government
www.dhhs.tas.gov.au/palliativecare/advance_care_planning
Planning Ahead Tools: Three easy ways to plan ahead
NSW Government
http://planningaheadtools.com.au/
Advance care planning
Have the conversation. A strategy for Victorian health services
2014-2018
www.health.vic.gov.au/acp
End of Life Care Pathway for Residential Aged Care Facilities. www.health.
qld.gov.au/cpcre/eol_pthwys.asp

Resources

Improving end of life care through the 7 Step Pathway
    Government of South Australia /www.sahealth.sa.gov.au/
    wps/wcm/connect/public+content/ sa+health+internet/
    clinical+resources/clinical+topics/end+of+life
    +for+health+professionals/resuscitation+plan+7+step+pathway
My Values: Your voice when you can't speak for yourself
    www.myvalues.org.au/
Respecting Patient Choices
    ACT Health
    http://health.act.gov.au/public-information/consumers/
    respecting-patient-choices
Advance Care Planning in Northern Territory.
    http://advancecareplanning.org.au/resources/northern-territory
Palliative Care Australia: Directory of Services
    http://palliativecare.org.au/directory-of-services/
Anastasios, A. *Dying to Know:Bringing death to life. Igniting Change.* 2014.
    Hardie Grant Books, Australia.
    www.thegroundswellproject.com/shop/dyingtoknow
Janca A, Bullen C. The Aboriginal Concept of Time and its Mental Health
    Implications. *Australasian Psychiatry* 2003; 11(1_suppl): S40–S44.
    doi.org/10.1046/j.1038-5282.2003.02009.x
Parker SM1, Clayton JM, Hancock K, Walder S, et al. A systematic review of
    prognostic/end-of-life communication with adults in the advanced
    stages of a life-limiting illness: patient/caregiver preferences,
    content, style, and timing of information. *J Pain Symptom Manage*
    2007; 34(1): 81-93.

North American resources

Make my Plan – The Speak Up Campaign, Canada
    www.advancecareplanning.ca/my-plan/
Why prepare and plan for serious illness (Canada)
    https://planwellguide.com/about-planwell/
Advance Care Planning
    National Institute on Ageing
    www.nia.nih.gov/health/caregiving/advance-care-planning
Tool Kit for Health Care Advance Planning, 3rd Ed 2020
    American Bar Association
    www.americanbar.org/content/dam/aba/administrative/law_
    aging/2020-tool-kit-hcap.pdf

Advance Directive Forms (State specific)
    American Association of Retired Persons (AARP)
    www.aarp.org/caregiving/financial-legal/free-printable-advance-
    directives/
Health Advocate Blog:
    Communicating your wishes for end-of-life care,
    11th September 2020
    http://blog.healthadvocate.com/2020/09/communicating-your-
    wishes-for-end-of-life-care/
Thinking Ahead: My Way, My Choice, My Life at the End
    The Coalition for Compassionate Care of California
    https://coalitionccc.org/wp-content/uploads/2014/01/Thinking-
    Ahead-Booklet_web.pdf
Loving Conversations (YouTube)
    American Health Law Association
    www.youtube.com/playlist?list=PLA263A3ECA01C9DAA
US Advance Care Plan Registry
    www.usacpr.net/
End-of-life Decisions: Honoring the Wishes of the Person with
    Alzheimer's Disease
    Alzheimer's Association
    www.alz.org/national/documents/brochure_endoflifedecisions.pdf
Palliative Care
    National Family Caregivers Association (NFCA)
    https://caringcommunity.org/topics/resources/palliative-care-
    and-hospice/
Give peace of mind: Advance Care Planning
    Centers for Disease Control and Prevention, USA
    www.cdc.gov/aging/advancecareplanning/
Advance Care Planning
    Centers for Disease Control and Prevention, USA
    www.cdc.gov/aging/advancecareplanning/
What is an Advance Health Directive? And Living Will? (USA)
    www.helpguide.org/articles/end-of-life/advanced-health-care-
    directives-and-living-wills.htm

Index